A Book of Mathematical and Reasoning Problems:

Fifty Brain Twisters

A Book of Mathematical and Reasoning Problems

Fifty Brain Twisters

by
D. ST. P. BARNARD

D. VAN NOSTRAND COMPANY, INC.

Princeton, New Jersey

Toronto London

New York

Printed in Great Britain

QA 95
·B3
1962

2.50

Preface

The problems that are to be found in this book have all appeared at one time or another in *The Observer*. Most of them have been taken from my *Brain-Twister* column, but some represent earlier problems published in that paper as Christmas competitions before the Brain-Twisters became established as a regular weekly feature.

In preparing the problems for publication in book form I have revised some of them where it has seemed to me that a bit on here or a bit off there might improve their presentation. This revision applies particularly to the solutions, some of which are here more fully expressed than was always possible within the columnar strait-jacket that any journal must necessarily impose on its features.

I have also inserted between the problems and their solutions a small section under the heading of 'Leads'. This section represents a new departure in the presentation of recreational problems. It is intended to aid the solver who may find a problem too elusive, but who may be able to solve it if given a hint or lead to set him off along the right lines. A certain degree of frustration is an essential element in the enjoyment of any puzzle but, if too prolonged, frustration may turn to fury. This we want to avoid. If therefore, after having given a problem a fair trial, the solver finds himself still baffled, he would be well advised to turn up the problem in the 'Leads' section, where he will find a suggestion or two which, while not divulging the answer, may enable him to mount a renewed attack on the question. If that should fail there still remains the full solution at the back of the book as an insurance against insomnia.

Readers who have solved a problem are also advised to refer to the appropriate Lead before verifying their answer in the Solutions at the end of the book. In some instances the Lead

Preface

indicates what is *not* the answer to a particular problem, and if, perchance, the reader discovers that he has arrived at one of these wrong answers, he can then go back to recheck his reasoning in an attempt to find the true answer before it is revealed by the Solution.

I take this opportunity to express my thanks to the proprietors of *The Observer* for their permission to reproduce the problems in book form. For problems Nos. 23 and 42 I have also to thank two friends, Group-Captain G. Struan Marshall, who devised *A Safe Number*, and Mr. Sinclair Grant, who was responsible for *Crow Flight*.

No list of acknowledgements is complete without a reference to that inevitable 'one without whom this book would never have been produced'. In this case that title belongs to my agents, Messrs. Rupert Crew Ltd., who were the first to suggest the publication of *The Observer Brain-Twisters* in book form.

Finally I must thank all those hundreds of people who have written to me from all parts of the world. Their many constructive suggestions have been of great help in the task of compiling and revising these problems.

D. St. P. B.

Cheltenham

Contents

Contents

The Problems

The two references given in bold at the foot of each problem indicate the pages on which the Lead and the Solution to the problem may be found. The purpose of the Lead is described in the Preface.

(1) ZOOLOGISTICS

'Oh, I'd be ever so much too frightened to go into the Wabe,' said Alice, 'because that is where the Jabberwock lives.'

'Nonsense!' declared the Mad Hatter. 'The Jabberwock lives on the top of a Tumtum tree.' He appealed to the other two for confirmation, and the March Hare and the Dormouse agreed.

'Perhaps,' went on the Mad Hatter, 'she is thinking of the Bandersnatch, which is an animal.'

'The Bandersnatch is a bird,' interrupted the March Hare.

'Oh yes, I'm sure it is a bird,' said Alice. 'Isn't it, Dormouse?' The Dormouse nodded, first in agreement and then in sleep.

'Talking of birds,' continued the March Hare, reaching for the butter, 'the Jubjub, which has four wings and feeds on Toves . . .'

'Which has *five* wings and feeds on Toves,' corrected the Mad Hatter as he hastily pocketed his watch.

'But surely it has four wings and feeds on *Borogoves*,' put in Alice, lifting the Dormouse from the teapot and shaking him gently.

'It has five wings and feeds on Raths,' murmured the Dormouse, and went back to sleep.

Whereupon, while they all moved up one, the Cheshire Cat, who is very wise and knows everything, rematerialized on a branch above their heads to announce grinningly that out of the four *zoologistical* facts each had asserted or assented to, two were true facts and two were false facts.

Then he redematerialized, which means that we have still to find out where the Jabberwock lives, what the Bandersnatch is, whether the Jubjub has four or five wings and what it feeds on.

Lead   **p. 59**
Solution **p. 71**

(2) SPINNING WHEEL

Mr. Lucker made his fortune out of cotton spinning, and when he died he left his six mills to his six nephews, Arthur, Barry,

The Problems

Charles, David, Ernest, and Frank. To avoid any appearance of favouritism he did not name which mill should be allocated to each nephew, but declared that the decision should be made, as had his money, by 'spinning'.

He provided a contrivance consisting of a hexagonal plate bearing the names of his six nephews, and, pivoted to the centre of this plate, a disc bearing the numbers 0–5.

Mr. Lucker's instructions were that the disc should be spun five times, and that the scores obtained by each boy on each spin should be totalled. The nephew gaining the highest total for the five spins was to have first choice of a mill, the nephew with the second highest total second choice, and so on.

The diagram shows the result of the first spin. On the second spin David forged ahead with his total to take the lead, but it was Arthur who, after five spins, obtained a total higher than anyone else's and who therefore had first choice.

What were the final totals for each of the six boys?

Lead   p. 59
Solution p. 71

The Problems

(3) COUPLING

Last year a married couple engaged my house-boat for a few weeks on the Broads. They brought with them their son and daughter. The son came with his wife, and the daughter with her husband. I had known all three couples at one time or another, and on their first evening aboard I was invited to take cocktails with the company.

Ethel was leaning on the rail talking to Charles's wife when I arrived. Poor Ethel; a few months earlier she had lost her only son in a motor accident, and she looked badly in need of a holiday. I could not help noticing her pallid complexion and drawn features when, a short while later, Ethel came over to where Doris had joined me for a vermouth. I found it hard to realize that the two women were exactly the same age.

I found Charles engaged in a friendly argument about the tennis achievements of their wives with Algernon (who, incidentally, inherited quite a tidy sum of money when his father died some years ago). Algernon's wife is older than Charles's, but I must say that she can still serve a sizzling ace. Bertrand, as the oldest member of the sextet and therefore presumably the most diplomatic, was called in to adjudicate, while I went over to join Frieda.

Which woman was the wife of which man, and which couple were the parents of whom? It is hardly necessary to add that none of the company had been previously married.

Lead   p. 59
Solution p. 72

(4) THE PLANTATION

On a certain jute plantation in Bengal the manager noticed that each morning before setting the team of workers their tasks for the day, the native overseer would line them all up round the boundary fence. He would then carefully pace out the distance between each man. The little ceremony piqued the manager's curiosity, and he therefore inquired the reason for this procedure.

'You say,' explained the overseer, 'that I am allowed one man to every acre of field, so, since the field is square, I place one man at each corner and the rest I make to stand round the four sides so that each man in the team is exactly the same distance from the two on either side of him. Then, if I find that each man is standing just twenty-two yards away from his neighbour, I know that I have my right allotment of men for the day.'

As it so happened, the overseer was perfectly right, but had the field been any larger or any smaller he would not have been. How many acres were there in the field?

Just in case you may have forgotten, there are 4,840 square yards in an acre.

Lead   p. 59

Solution p. 73

(5)   UNEVEN ODDS

As though they weren't pitching and tossing and rolling enough already, two bored travellers on the S.S. *Betterman* were killing time in the saloon by rolling dice.

'Look here,' said Henshaw. 'The highest total I can throw with these two dice is twelve, and half of twelve is six. Agreed?'

'Agreed,' said Blithering.

'Then,' proposed Henshaw, 'I will lay even money that on my first throw the total on the two dice will be at least six.'

'Oh, no you don't,' protested Blithering. 'I'm not such an idiot as all that; I've been caught like that before. But I'll tell you what I will do. I will lay 10s. to say that you *won't* throw a total of at least six, if you will give me fair odds.'

'And what would you consider to be fair odds?' asked Henshaw.

'Well, to tell you the truth, I'm blessed if I know,' admitted Blithering.

Now if the odds were to be perfectly fair, and if Blithering were to lay 10s. on Henshaw *not* throwing a total of at least six, how much should Henshaw have been prepared to wager that he *would* throw a total of at least six?

Lead   p. 59

Solution p. 73

(6) CONUNDRA ZOO

On taking charge of the Conundra Zoo, the new curator was disturbed to find that, by some mischance, the animals were all accommodated in the wrong cages. A notice above each cage indicated where each animal should be, but the tiger was in the lion's cage, the gorilla in the rhino's, the rhino in the bear's, the lion in the gorilla's, and the bear in the tiger's.

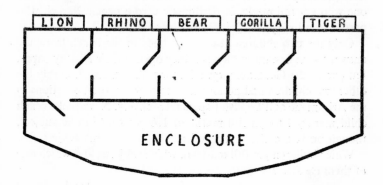

He ordered the keeper to move the animals immediately into their proper cages but, since they were all ferocious beasts, it was unthinkable that any two should be permitted to occupy the same cage, or even to be together in the enclosure, at the same time. What is the least number of moves the keeper would have had to make in order to carry out the curator's instructions, and in what sequence would he have had to move the beasts?

Lead p. 59
Solution p. 74

(7) FULL MARKS

On a straight bench were seated four children, Mabel, John, Betty, and Tom (though not necessarily in that order) for an examination in Arithmetic, Geography, English, and History.

B   17

The Problems

Two of them happened to be twins, and were separated by the master who placed one other child in between them.

The twins were first to finish, perhaps because they used pencils whereas the other two children had to keep dipping their pens into the ink, but one of the twins failed in English and the other in Geography.

The child who got full marks in English passed in Geography, but the last child of all to finish, failed in Geography. Of the two girls (who, by the way, were not sitting next to one another) the one who got full marks in Arithmetic used a pencil. Mabel, who passed in all subjects, finished earlier than John.

Only the two children at opposite ends of the bench knew the answer to the first question when they opened their History paper, but one of the Geography questions stumped them. Similarly the other two children had no idea how to tackle certain questions in the Arithmetic and English papers respectively. Nevertheless each child managed to get full marks of 100 per cent in one subject, though no two children got full marks in the same subject.

Which children got full marks in which subjects, and which one of them cheated?

Lead   p. 60
Solution p. 74

(8)   VENUSIAN FEELERS

Mathematically there is nothing sacrosanct about the number Ten. We rely on it so much only because we happen to have ten fingers. Had humans possessed only four fingers, instead of being taught to count 1, 2, 3, 4, 5, 6, 7, 8, 9, 10, 11, etc., we should undoubtedly have been taught to say 1, 2, 3, 10, 11, 12, 13, 20, 21, 22, 23, and so on. Instead of saying $3 + 5 = 8$, we should then have had to say $3 + 11 = 20$.

Such considerations might well prove embarrassing to space travellers if certain science-fiction writers are to be believed. For instance, it has been suggested that the inhabitants of Venus may have, not hands and fingers, but a number of feelers sprouting from their high-domed foreheads. If so, it would seem probable that they would have learned to count, not up to ten, but up to the number of feelers they possess. Thus, we might imagine the following sort of conversation:

INTREPID EARTHMAN: I notice that, up here, you produce much bigger families than we do on earth. May I inquire just how many children you have?

VENUSIAN (*Scratching back of head with feeler*): Yes, now let me see. I have 43 sons, and—er—52 daughters. That makes 125 altogether, doesn't it?

Assuming the Venusian's calculation was, from his point of view, correct, how many children (in our earthly figures) did he have, and how many feelers sprout from a Venusian's high-domed forehead?

Lead   p. 60
Solution p. 75

(9)   HOLIDAY PLANS

'It is an island, isn't it?'

'Just,' said Uncle Cryptopher, with his pedantic predilection for precise definition. 'But it is beautiful and, if it is the weather you are thinking of, it is fine and sunny.'

'I'm wondering how it would do for my wife.'

'Since she's a blonde it would suit her perfectly. How is she, by the way?'

'So-so.'

'You see, that is exactly what I mean!'

'Of course, what she is really interested in when on holidays is souvenir hunting.'

'She might get a small article in wood from the island.'

'What does it provide in the way of meals?'

'Nothing but sound food.'

'Actually, I was thinking of going to some place where I could get in a little golfing practice. My game is not that good, you know.'

'Then the island is just such a place. Moreover, it has a way with it for golfers.'

'You're not trying to pull the wool over my eyes?'

'Not at all, though I must admit that if you were to take it all upon yourself you would be doing just that. To be honest, some might call it a big sell, but then the children always love it.'

'Yes, but how does one get the passage money?'

'Just say the word!'

'Then I'll go.'

WHERE?

Lead   p. 60

Solution p. 75

(10)   CHANGING WAYS

The newsagent counted the odd assortment of coins I had fished out of my pocket: a sixpence, a threepence, ten pennies, and six halfpennies.

'That's right,' he said, 'one shilling and ten pence. But do you know that legally I could refuse to accept these coins as payment for that amount?'

'How is that?' I inquired.

'You have copper coins there to the value of 1s. 1d., and copper is legal tender only up to the amount of one shilling. Of course,' he went on with a wink, 'I shouldn't keep my trade for long if I were to insist on legal quibbles like that. Actually I can do with a bit of extra change in my till, and it would be quite all right by me if you were to produce twenty-two pennies or forty-four halfpennies for that matter.'

Which set me wondering as to how many different ways there are in which it is possible to offer the exact sum of 1s. 10d:

(a) *to* my obliging newsagent?

(b) *to* a less obliging one who insisted on his legal right to accept no more than the sum of one shilling in copper?

(Remember, farthings are no longer recognized as currency, and should not be used in either case.)

Lead   p. 60

Solution p. 76

The Problems

(11) PYTHON GORGE

So fierce was competition between prospectors during the great gold-rush of the last century that the licensing authorities at Python Gorge were compelled to limit the area that could be claimed by any one man to three square chains. Moreover, to discourage gerrymandering, they insisted that every claim should be staked out in the form of a square. And, of course, no prospector was permitted more than one claim.

These restrictions proved more than a headache for old Joe Matheman who arrived at the diggings with nothing more than a piece of rope just two chains long, half a dozen pegs, and a vague feeling that the name of the gorge reminded him faintly of something he had once learnt at school.

However, old Joe was resolved to peg out his full entitlement and, by dint of some manipulation of the rope, together with sundry lines scratched by his pegs on the flat, dry, dusty surface of the ground, he managed eventually to do so.

Can you suggest a way in which he could have accomplished the task?

Lead   p. 60
Solution p. 76

(12) MONEY FOR JAM

The following is an extract from last October's issue of *Wit's Once Weekly*. The fact that the magazine failed to publish the full solution to their competition aroused my suspicions, and I took the trouble to check the accuracy of the statement reproduced below. I found that so far as it goes the statement is honest enough in content, if not in intention.

It's ready ! ! ! The big 'Money for Jam' competition announced last month in WIT'S ONCE WEEKLY *has finally been decided! Remember? We printed a whole row of numbered jam jars with a name label beneath each (the wrong label of course—we told you that, didn't we? Ha, ha!) And you had to cut the labels out, juggle 'em round, and stick the right ones on the right jars—for a First*

The Problems

Prize of £100, and a second of £50! You did your best; yes, siree, you did! Over 6,000 of you got exactly half the jars correctly labelled, and 4,960 of you got exactly two-thirds of them right! But no one, not a single one of you, got them all right ! ! !

Does that mean no prizes ? Not on your life, as the hangman said to the bookie! The cash (oh, that lovely boodle!) is already on its way to those who came closest. First prize goes to Mr. Wattsitt of Sumwarethare, who topped the list with 17 correct, and Second prize has been shared equally between 60 lucky people who managed to get 16 right. What could be fairer than that?

Well, that is the question: what could be fairer than that?

Lead   p. 60
Solution p. 78

(13)   PIPER'S TANK

Mr. Piper, the local plumber, was approached on one occasion by a customer who, having discovered a rectangular sheet of iron in his outhouse, decided to have it made into a new water tank for his attic. The sheet of iron measured 10 ft. 8 in. by 8 ft., and from this he asked Mr. Piper to construct a simple, rectangular tank. No top was necessary for, as is usual with such tanks, he proposed to cover it with wooden boards.

The dimensions of the tank he left to Mr. Piper, but on one point the customer was insistent: in order to make the most economical use of the iron, the dimensions were to be such that the tank would contain the greatest possible quantity of water.

Mr. Piper, a plumber of some mathematical knowledge and ingenuity, carried out his customer's instructions faithfully. What was the capacity (to the nearest gallon) of the tank he supplied?

(One cubic foot of water contains $6\frac{1}{4}$ gallons; at least, that is a close enough approximation, and is the formula that should be used.)

Lead   p. 60
Solution p. 78

22

The Problems

(14) THE LOST CODE

There was consternation at the Colonial Residency; someone had lost the code-book, and an urgent telegram had just arrived from somewhere up-country.

SVMKRF VQ VSS EPZVPEF EKTYNXRI PF FPIIKFA TRIKE
XF UPXYWKRXRI. XR ZC JXKO STRIKE FHVAF TEK
GVZGTM TRS DTZGTMT. X ZPFA NTJK T GXA VQ TXS
PH NKEK GC RKLA BTRPTEC.

                      NKRFNTO

Try as he might, the Resident could make neither head nor tail of it, yet dared not risk the delay of sending for a duplicate code-book.

Fortunately, with the aid of nothing other than his knowledge of the rules of English spelling and a happy knack of putting two and two together, one of the Resident's aides managed to break the cipher and transcribe the message. This much only was known of the code; that it was a 'substitution' code, that is to say, each letter consistently represents some other particular letter of the alphabet.

What message did the telegram contain?

Lead   p. 61
Solution p. 78

(15) FIGURE IT OUT

The arrangements of letters overleaf represent three arithmetical calculations. In each example each letter stands for a corresponding digit, and the purpose of the problem is to discover which digit each letter represents. Each example can be solved by the application of simple arithmetic and logical reasoning, and there is only one possible answer to each. So that you can gradually warm up to the task, they have been arranged in increasing order of difficulty.

(i) Addition

```
        X   R   B   X
        T   R   X
    +       T   X
    ─────────────────
        B   R   T   X
```

(ii) Multiplication

```
            H   L   P
        ×       H   P
        ─────────────
            A   M   F
        Z   Q   C
        ─────────────
        C   H   L   F
```

(iii) Division

```
                          K   S
    W   J   D ) W   G   V   K   W
               W   S   N   S
               ─────────────
                   K   Y   W
                   D   D   N
                   ─────────────
                   N   K   N
```

Lead   p. 61
Solution p. 79

(16)   COLOUR COMBINATIONS

The diagrams below represent a pyramid, a cube, and an equilateral tetrahedron (i.e. a three-sided pyramid, all four surfaces of which are identical equilateral triangles).

 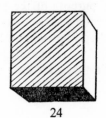 

The Problems

Using five different colours, it is possible to colour the pyramid's five surfaces in just thirty *essentially different* ways. Thus if you were to paint thirty pyramids in these ways, and then tried to paint the thirty-first differently, you would discover that your new combination could really have been obtained merely by twisting round one of the original thirty so that a different side faced you.

(i) In how many *essentially different* ways is it possible to paint the six faces of a cube with six different colours, using all six colours each time? (Remember, a cube may not only be turned round on its base, but may also be rolled in several different directions.)

(ii) In how many *essentially different* ways is it possible to paint the four faces of an equilateral tetrahedron with four different colours, using all four colours each time? The answer to this one may well surprise you.

Lead   p. 61
Solution p. 80

(17)   TIDDLYWINKS

This problem actually arose, and was referred to me, when two English universities challenged one another to a Tiddlywinks match. According to the rules for such matches, each team is made up of four pairs. (We shall call the four pairs representing the Home Team A, B, C, D, and the four pairs representing the Visiting Team a, b, c, d.) During the match each pair of the Home Team plays every pair of the Visiting Team. The match itself is divided into four rounds, with four games played simultaneously in each round.

Now the Home Team possessed four mats, the surfaces of which varied considerably. In order to be absolutely fair, it was therefore decided that each pair should play one of its games on each mat.

A chart was drawn up, and this is how the captains started allocating the teams:

	Mat 1	*Mat 2*	*Mat 3*	*Mat 4*
Round 1	Aa	Bb	Cc	
Round 2	Bc			
Round 3	C			
Round 4				

How should the remainder of the chart be completed? There is only one possible solution.

Lead   p. 61
Solution p. 81

(18)   CROWN, ORB, AND SCEPTRE

When King Charles of Calcularia died, the main provisions of his will were that his kingdom should be ruled jointly by his three sons, in token whereof he bequeathed to his eldest son the Crown, to his second son the Orb, and to his youngest son the Sceptre.

The king's treasure, which consisted of twenty sealed chests of gold, was to be disposed of thus: to the children of his eldest son three chests each; to the children of his second son two chests each; and to the children of his youngest son one chest each. The remainder of the chests were to be divided equally between King Charles's own daughters.

Now the names of the king's sons (in alphabetical order) were Albert, Ferdinand, and Joseph. Albert had two sons of his own, Ferdinand three daughters, and Joseph two sons and two daughters. The provisions of the will in respect of the chests would therefore have worked out neatly, but on the eve of the king's own death one of his grandsons died. To avoid argument, the chest or chests that would have gone to this child were added to those already allocated to King Charles's daughters, and an equal number of chests was given to each of them. Thus were all the chests accounted for.

What were the names of the sons who received the Crown, the Orb, and the Sceptre, respectively? And whose child was it that died on the eve of the king's death?

Lead   p. 61
Solution p. 82

26

(19)   PASTRY-CUTTER

Who has not, at one time or another, either as child or adult, amused himself by making patterns with a pastry-cutter? You know the sort of thing I mean; a sharp metal ring used for pressing out scones or biscuits from a slab of raw paste.

While watching my wife rolling out scones one day, it occurred to me to wonder just how many pieces a single circle of pastry could be divided into by seven cuts of the same implement that had originally been used to cut the circle from the slab.

The diagram shows how, by three cuts, the original circle could be divided into seven pieces.

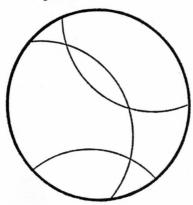

What is the maximum number of pieces that could be produced by seven cuts?

Naturally, one is not permitted to rearrange the pieces after cutting; the pieces must be allowed to remain in their original relative positions until the process has been completed.

Lead   p. 62
Solution p. 83

(20)   SHARE PRICES

Dear Sir,
    I have your letter of yesterday's date instructing me to buy on

*your behalf 105 O.B.T. shares, 75 Geomercantiles, and 30 Adding-
tons, representing a total investment of £100. As your stockbroker,
may I point out that this is rather an unbalanced packet? I suggest
that I invest that sum for you by buying 60 shares in each of the
companies mentioned.*

Yours faithfully,

I. C. BONDS.

Long experience has taught me to accept my stockbroker's
advice, so I immediately agreed to Mr. Bonds's suggestion.

As it turned out he was unable to procure any Geomercantiles,
so he invested my £100 by buying an equal number of O.B.T.s
and Addingtons. The result of his so doing was that I finished up
with 60 shares fewer than I had originally planned for in my
'unbalanced packet'.

What was the price of a share in each of the three companies
mentioned? I should, of course, mention that the prices of the
shares remained static during the course of our correspondence
and dealings.

Lead   p. 62
Solution p. 84

(21)   DIGITAL WANDERERS

The eleven members of the Digital Wanderers Cricket Team
were exceptionally wealthy men and, to encourage sport, they
decided to donate, as a club, to the National Playing Fields
Association exactly £1 for every run their club had ever scored
since its inception in 1860, each of the eleven men to contribute
equally towards this sum. As it so happened this worked out just
nicely, but as they were about to send off the money their eleven
small sons turned up with an additional donation to which they
too had each contributed equally. It was a very small donation,
totalling not even £1, but small gifts are not to be despised. The
sum the boys had collected was added to the club's donation and
a cheque sent off for the whole amount.

Now the peculiar thing about this cheque was that the figures in the total were an arrangement of the digits 1 to 9, each of which digits appeared once and once only. For instance, had each of the boys contributed 5*d*. and each of the fathers £138,536, the cheque would have totalled £1,523,896 4s. 7d., which amount contains each of the nine digits once and once only, but actually the cheque was for a somewhat smaller amount.

What is the smallest possible amount that could have been shown on the cheque? For that matter, what, too, could have been the largest possible amount—if the team had been consistently mammoth scorers?

Remember, halfpennies and farthings cannot be shown on a cheque.

Lead   p. 62
Solution p. 84

(22)   CALCULARI'S CONCERTS

During his last series of four concerts Calculari, the well-known pianist, performed works by Beethoven, Brahms, Mozart, Liszt, and Chopin.

In each concert he played four works, each of the four works being by a different composer. However, no two concerts in the series included the same four composers in the same order.

He never played Mozart and Beethoven in the same concert, but if he omitted Beethoven he always played a Mozart, followed immediately by a Chopin. On the other hand, if Mozart were omitted, Calculari always finished his concert with a work by Brahms. The pianist also followed his invariable rule of commencing a concert with Liszt if Brahms happened to be anywhere in the programme.

The first three of Calculari's concerts finished with a work by the same composer. What composers did he play in his fourth and final concert, and in what order where they played?

Lead   p. 62
Solution p. 85

The Problems

(23)   A SAFE NUMBER

I ran into Quaddle the other day. He was outside the lock-smith's, and looking very pleased with himself. It turned out that he had just devised a sort of super-mnemonic for recalling a number that would tell those who were in the know how many turns to give the knob in order to open a safe door.

'As a matter of fact, old boy'—I do wish he would not use that term for me who am neither old nor a boy—'there's no reason why I shouldn't tell you about it, for the safe is going abroad and you will certainly never see it. The number is the smallest number which, when multiplied by its last (or right hand) digit is changed by having that digit transferred from the end of the number to the beginning.'

As this was rather obscure he produced a piece of paper and explained, 'Take the number

$$101123595505617977752808988764044943820224719.$$

If we multiply it by its last digit (9) we get

$$910112359550561797775280898876404494382022471,$$

which is the original number with the last digit transferred to the front, but this is certainly not the smallest such number.'

'How about 11?' I suggested brightly.

'Ridiculous!' expostulated Quaddle. 'I said distinctly that the number *changed*.'

What was the number that would open Quaddle's safe?

Lead   **p. 62**
Solution p. 85

(24)   COURT CARDS

From a pack of cards select an Ace, King, Queen, Jack, and Ten which should be stacked, as shown, in the uppermost of three circles drawn thus:

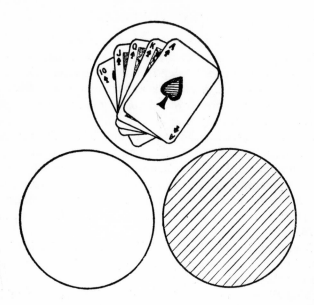

The problem is now to move the cards *one at a time* from one circle to another until all are restacked in their original order in the shaded circle. However, at no time must a card of lower value be placed on a card of higher value. Of course only the top card of any stack may be touched; to shorten the process by abstracting cards from the bottom of the stack would not be quite *comme il faut.*

With patience and perseverance you should be able to complete the task sooner or later, but what is the smallest number of moves in which it can be accomplished?

Moreover, what would be the smallest possible number of moves if all the eight cards of a Piquet suit (i.e. the A, K, Q, J, 10, 9, 8, 7) were to be used? Or, for that matter, a whole bridge suit of thirteen cards?

Lead   p. 62
Solution p. 86

The Problems

LONG DIVISION

Factorization leads to some interesting and useful short cuts in calculation. For instance it is useful to know that *If the sum of the digits in an even number is divisible by 3 then the number itself is divisible by 6.* Again, it is rather interesting to learn that *Every prime number greater than 6 would, if increased or decreased by 1, become divisible by 6.*

Sometimes a problem can be solved only by devising new rules. Naturally, in making these rules, one must be careful to avoid false assumptions. For example, one might be tempted to suppose that if a number is divisible by two other numbers then it is also divisible by the product of those numbers, but this is not necessarily so; 36 is divisible by 6 and also by 4, but is not divisible by 24.

Here, then, is a problem which, if you are to solve it without the aid of an electronic computer, you will need to discover some rule or rules to help you.

Using all the ten digits 0–9 each time, they may be combined to form 3,265,920 different numbers, of which the largest is 9,876,543,210, and the smallest 1,023,456,789. (Since 0,123,456,789 starts with a zero it is not, strictly speaking, a true number and all such combinations should be disregarded.)

The question is, how many of these 3,265,920 numbers are divisible by 72?

Lead   p. 63
Solution p. 86

(26)   RIDDLETON BY-ELECTION

TORIES HOLD SAFE SEAT

Liberal Gains—Independent Loses Deposit

Despite a small drop in the Conservative vote, the Riddleton by-election resulted in an easy win for the Conservative candidate, who was returned with a majority of 7,895 over his nearest opponent.

The Problems

A feature of this five-cornered contest was the exceptionally heavy poll; 87.5 per cent of the electorate voted, compared with 76 per cent in the 1955 General Election when the Conservative gained an absolute majority of 2,335 over his two opponents. On that occasion there were 2,739 fewer electors on the roll than this time.

One of the most striking features of the by-election was the ousting of Labour from second place by the Liberal candidate, who secured 1,230 more votes than his Labour opponent. At the 1955 election Labour, with exactly two-fifths of the total votes cast, was only 4,977 behind the Conservative.

Mr. Freer, the Independent candidate, failed by less than ten votes to save his deposit. Mr. Freer, who polled exactly seven times as many votes as the Communist candidate, described as ridiculous the rule that a candidate must forfeit his £150 if he fails to receive one-eighth of the total votes cast.

Which may all be very interesting, but how many votes did each candidate receive at the Riddleton by-election?

Lead   **p. 63**
Solution p. 87

(27)   A MATTER OF X-ERCISE

Despite its title, this problem does not necessarily involve the use of Xs, Ys, and Zs. You may employ them if you wish, but what really concerns us is the question of physical exercise, namely that taken by a certain Mr. Ernest Quation.

Mr. Quation lived at Aixville from where, during the summer months, he would ride by horse to Beeton, a journey that by this mode of transport took him just 40 minutes. From Beeton he would walk the long, straight, ten-mile road to Seaview where, feeling tired, he would hire a bicycle to ride back to Aixville. By riding the bicycle at a steady 12 m.p.h. he could travel three times as quickly as he could on foot, with the result that he invariably arrived back just $3\frac{1}{2}$ hours after setting out from home.

The Problems

During the winter months he would reverse the routine by riding on horseback to Seaview before walking the ten miles to Beeton and, from there, cycling back to Aixville, a procedure that also took $3\frac{1}{2}$ hours.

Assuming he always rode, walked, and cycled at constant speeds, that he always used the same roads, and that he lost no time in changing from one form of locomotion to another, how many miles was his round trip in all?

Worked it out already? Just check over your reasoning to make sure you haven't overlooked some little point.

Lead   p. 63
Solution p. 88

(28)   ROOKERY

When the Black Rook (who, of course, is not permitted to move diagonally) was invited, in defiance of all protocol, to take tea with the White Rook, the question arose as to what would be the shortest route for him to take.

'If I were you I would go somehow like this,' declared the Black Knight, indicating the route marked 'A' in the diagram,

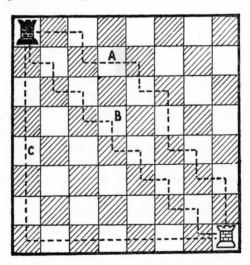

The Problems

but the Bishop maintained that it would be shorter to take the route he marked 'B'.

'Nonsense,' said the Black Queen, 'the shortest route is obviously this one that I have marked "C".'

It was left to the wise old King to point out that all three routes suggested were exactly the same length, which raised the question (if we may use an antilogy): Just how many shortest routes are there by which the Black Rook could reach the White Rook's square?

Lead   p. 63
Solution p. 89

(29)   PIN-POINTING SABOTAGE

The racing circuit at Trackville is not large; a mere quarter of a mile in diameter, but it is much favoured for speed trials on account of both its even surface and its perfect circularity. It was, perhaps, for this reason that F. O. R. Stroke chose the course for his attempt to break the world track speed record on his new A.R.C. motor-cycle.

It is regrettable to report that a serious attempt was made to sabotage the run. An odd glint of light at the very top of the wheel which showed up on the high-speed photograph taken just as the motor-cycle completed its circuit, led to an examination of the machine and revealed that a drawing-pin had been inserted in the front tyre of Stroke's machine. It had not been noticed at the start of the race for the saboteur (later identified as an unscrupulous rival by the unfortunate name of Spike Wheeler) had taken care to insert it at the bottom of the wheel where the tyre on the starting line touched the ground. Fortunately the pin proved to be too short and, instead of being thrust up through the tread, had been carried round and round in the tyre for the whole of the circuit, in what would have been a series of curves.

How far did that pin travel during Stroke's circuit of the course? Minor factors such as tilt and offset may be ignored.

Lead   p. 63
Solution p. 89

The Problems

(30)   PIP POKER

While Mr. and Mrs. Addishon were playing their after-dinner
game of Bezique, their four children amused themselves by trying
to play poker with the low cards their parents had discarded from
the two standard packs.

The youngsters knew that each player should have five cards,
and four hands were dealt accordingly.

'Has anyone got a pair?' cried the youngest.

'Oh, pairs aren't worth much,' sneered his neighbour. 'Has
anyone got three of a kind?'

They all examined their hands, but no child held three cards all
of the same value; not that it mattered much because they decided
that it would be fairest if they all just added up the total number
of pips each held in his or her hand to see who had the most.

This they did, but only to find that each of them held exactly
the same number of pips, though no two hands were exactly alike.
So they all threw in their hands—and there on the table lay
5 Sixes, 5 Twos, 4 Fives, 4 Threes, and 2 Fours.

How had each of the four hands been made up?

Lead   p. 64
Solution p. 90

(31)   RUNNING TO TIME

Farmer Roots's property was square in shape and covered an
area of exactly two square miles. It was divided (as shown in the
diagram) into four fields. The large, shaded field was one mile
square.

The farmhouse was situated at one corner of the smaller square
field, which field also had at its other corners a well, an empty
cottage, and a stile.

Each morning young Tom, the farmer's son, kept himself in
training by running from the house to the stile and back again.
On one occasion he started off from the house just as Farmer

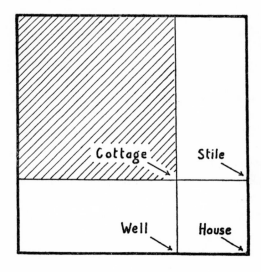

Roots himself left the house to visit the cottage, walking by way of the well. On his way back from the stile Tom suddenly remembered that, in his pocket, was the cottage key which his father would undoubtedly need. On reaching the house therefore, instead of stopping, Tom continued to run, following the same path as his father had taken. He caught up with his father, handed over the key, and doubled back the way he had come.

Tom got back to the house at exactly the same time that his father reached the cottage. Assuming that Tom ran, and his father walked, at constant speeds all the time, and that no time was lost either in Tom's turning at the stile or in his handing over the key, how far did Tom run altogether?

Lead   p. 64
Solution p. 91

37

The Problems

CHECKING PRECEDENT

The rules of etiquette in the old Checkoslomate court were strict indeed, and the order of precedence was: K, Q, KR, QR, KB, QB, KKt, QKt.

With the passing of the centuries, many antiquated and often confusing decrees had been enacted, e.g.:

THE COURT EGRESS ACT (Golombekski IV). *Apart from His Majesty, no member of the court may leave the royal palace without the instant permission of his or her immediate superior.*

THE RESPECT OF AUTHORITY ACT (Lingovitch XII). *No member of the court shall presume to authorize anything unless he or she be the senior member of the court resident in the palace at the time.*

THE NON–INTERVENTION ACT (Chodalex II). *No courtier shall bother his seniors with matters pertaining to his juniors.*

The literal interpretation of these rules caused many difficulties. For instance, if QR happened to be absent from the palace, KB could not obtain from him permission to leave. Again, even if QR happened to be there, KB could still not leave if K, Q, or KR were there, for their presence would deprive QR of all authority, and the Non-Intervention Act would prevent QR from seeking higher approval for KB's departure.

These complications became quite nightmarish when it was decided to move the court from the old palace to a new one, especially since the same rules were held to apply to each palace. Things may not have been so bad had the courtiers been able to assemble outside the old palace and move in one body to the new, but the prevalence of brigands in the surrounding countryside made this too dangerous a procedure and, quite understandably, each member of the court, on leaving one palace, would make straight for the safety of the other.

In what order should the pieces have moved if the court was to complete its transfer in the least possible number of moves? Each time a piece is touched counts as one move.

Lead p. 64
Solution p. 92

(33) BARBER'S POLE

Very smart looks my barber's newly painted pole with its red and white spiralled bands separated by thin gold and silver lines, each line circling the pole three and a half times.

The other day I noticed two flies, one perched on the nethermost point of the gold line (at the spot marked x) and the other on the supernal point of the silver line (at the spot marked y). They were then, so I afterwards ascertained, exactly $31\frac{1}{2}$ inches apart.

Now as I watched, the fly from x started to walk up the gold line at the same moment and at the same speed that the fly from y started to walk down the silver line. How far had each of the flies travelled when both were the same distance from the knob at the top of the pole?

The circumference of the pole, I should have told you, is 12 inches, and in case anyone should want to know the value of π, 3.141592653589793 is a close enough approximation.

Lead p. 64
Solution p. 92

(34) NOUGHTS AND CROSSES

The four diagrams below represent the final outcome of four games of Noughts and Crosses. A and B represent legitimate games, but not so the other two diagrams—in C, 'Nought' has

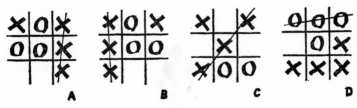

A   B   C   D

obviously missed a turn; in D, 'Cross' had already won on the bottom line before 'Nought' claimed his top-line win.

How many diagrams would be needed to represent the final outcome of *all* the possible *legitimate* games of Noughts and Crosses which result in a win for one of the players?

We are not interested in how wisely or how foolishly the opponents play so long as each game is legitimate. Notice that A and B count as two diagrams, although B is merely a reflection of A. Remember too, that a game may be started either by the 'Nought' player or by the 'Cross' player. And one final word of warning; when this problem first appeared, certain rare types of legitimate wins were specifically excluded by the inclusion of an extra diagram. This restriction is now removed. *All* legitimate wins must be accounted for.

Lead   **p. 64**
Solution p. 93

(35)   MULTIPLE MOTORS

The following is a list of the second-hand cars offered for sale by Multiple Motors Ltd. at their showrooms in Divisors one day last summer:

STRAITLEY Sal.	1957	£860
CHEETAH, 3.4 litre	1955	£425
DALEMAN MANX	1958	£425
GRIMSBY GROUSE	1955	£399
OXBRIDGE Sal.	1948	£165
ANGERLEY Sports	1939	£140
NOMAD, 14	1939	£132
ENSIGN, 10	1939	£124
COTTONSLEY, 14	1935	£68
ENGOUT SEVEN	1934	£53

The proprietor, who is known to me, says that trade was brisk during the morning and several cars were sold but, during the afternoon, the takings were even better; in fact the total value of the cars sold in the afternoon was *exactly* twice that of the cars sold during the morning.

The Problems

At the end of the day only one car was still left unsold in the showrooms.

Which cars were sold during the morning, which during the afternoon, and which car remained?

Lead   p. 64
Solution p. 94

(36)   CIRCLE OF FATE

The King of Cryptonia had long determined that his only daughter, the beautiful Princess Problema, should be betrothed on her seventeenth birthday but, as the day approached, he found himself quite unable to decide which of the seventeen young nobles who by rank and character were eligible as suitors was the most worthy to claim her hand.

He therefore decided to leave the matter in the hands of fate and, on her birthday, summoned Problema to the throne-room where he had commanded her seventeen suitors to form a circle thus:

41

The Problems

'My dearest daughter,' said the King, 'the time has come when you must wed, and I have determined that Fate shall choose from these young nobles your future spouse. But it is you who shall be the instrument of Fate, for it is my will that you shall stand in the centre of this circle and, counting from left to right, dismiss every third man till there remains but one, and him you shall marry.'

Then, to indicate where the princess should commence, the King gave to one man a small gold cross to hold. Calling this man number 'One', Problema started counting clockwise, dismissing every third man.

Suddenly she stopped for, to her dismay, she saw out of the corner of her eye that the very next man to be dismissed would be the young Count Algebar whom secretly she loved dearly.

In desperation she appealed to the King, saying, 'Father, to turn constantly in this direction makes me giddy. May I not count back the other way instead?'

Now the King, seeing that there were still quite a number of men left, took pity on her and agreed. So Problema, starting from the gap that had been created by the dismissal of the last suitor, went on counting, 'One, Two Three', and dismissing every third man of those remaining—but this time she counted from right to left.

Imagine her joy when, on finishing her task, there remained as the last man her own beloved Algebar, whom she married that very day, so that they lived happily ever after.

In what position must the Count Algebar have been standing?

Lead   p. 64
Solution p. 95

(37)   A PIECE OF CAKE

This is a true story.

For the first anniversary of my Brain-Twister column in *The Observer* I had presented to me a birthday cake. To eat it all myself would have seemed greedy; to have distributed it between all the thousands of people who, at one time or another, had entered for the Brain-Twister competitions would have been impracticable. I decided therefore to share it between the five prize winners for that week's problem, and the cake itself posed that very problem.

What I proposed to do was to divide the large cake into five small cakes which, like the original, should themselves be square and of the same thickness as the original cake. But dividing a square into five equal squares (with no wastage) calls for some ingenuity, and I therefore asked solvers to suggest the minimum number of pieces into which the cake would have to be cut in order that I should be able to fit together the five small ones. This they did, some economically and some not quite so economically.

The cake was then cut, the pieces jig-sawed together, and the five small cakes were duly despatched to the senders of the first five correct solutions checked.

How did I cut my cake?

(Oh yes, I know I cut it with a knife; what I really want to know are the directions in which I made the cuts.)

Lead   p. 65
Solution p. 96

(38)   EXTENSIVE REASONING

The unshaded portion of the diagram shows the Maidenfield Cricket Ground as it was originally, 110 yards across from A to C, and circular in shape except where a road cut across the eastern boundary, making B to D 22 yards shorter than A to C.

After several complaints from bowlers to the effect that the ground belied its name, the club decided to extend the western boundary. This was done by dismantling that semicircular part of the boundary fence marked ABC, and re-erecting it at EFG, so that the boundary distance FD was now the same as AC. The resulting gaps between A and E, and between C and G, were then filled in with new, straight fencing.

The newly acquired land (represented by the shaded area) was valued at £40 an acre, but unfortunately no one could work out the exact size of this additional area, and an argument arose between the owner of the ground and the club. The club secretary

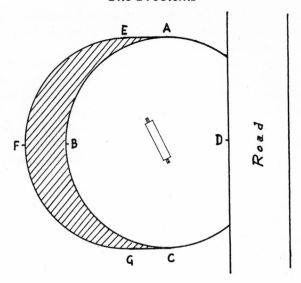

was about to call in surveyors to settle the point when his young son declared that it was a ridiculously easy calculation, and that he could easily work it out in his head—an announcement that surprised his father not a little for, although the boy was an ingenious young rascal, he had never been particularly good at arithmetic.

How much *exactly* should the club have paid for the additional land?

Lead   p. 65
Solution p. 97

(39)   THE GIFTS OF THE MAGI

A Christmas Story

We have often been told how the Three Wise Men, Gaspar, Melchior, and Balthazar, brought with them gifts of gold and frankincense and myrrh to the manger in Bethlehem, but no one has ever learned which of the three carried which gift. One man,

The Problems

however, did try to discover the secret—Herod, who, being covetous, sent an officer after their caravan to make inquiries, and to rob the magus who carried the gold.

The officer's inquiries were complicated by the fact that the Three Wise Men journeyed with three servants also named Gaspar, Melchior, and Balthazar, each like his respective master. Indeed, since each servant at times carried his own master's box, there was nothing to distinguish servants from masters except that the Three Wise Men invariably told the truth whereas their servants were such confirmed liars that it was impossible for them to make a truthful statement, save to acknowledge honestly enough their names and the names of their masters.

The officer, riding hard, caught up with the caravan one evening about dusk. Outside an inn he found three men, each bearing a box in his arms, while a little way off three others were tending the camels by a well.

Approaching the men with the boxes, the officer inquired first of the man called Gaspar if he were the one carrying the gold, but Gaspar, being under a vow to speak no language but his own, answered the question in Persian, a language the officer did not understand.

'What did he say?' demanded the officer, turning to the others.

'He said,' volunteered Melchior, 'that he is not the one carrying the gold.'

'Then what is it that you carry?' asked the officer.

'I,' said Melchior, 'carry the frankincense.'

'Is that true?' demanded the officer, wheeling on the third man.

'Yes, Melchior speaks truthfully,' replied Balthazar.

'Then you have the gold?'

'No,' said Balthazar, 'it is not I who carry the gold.'

'Then what,' asked the perplexed officer, 'is the first man carrying?'

'Gaspar,' explained Melchior, 'is carrying the incense.'

Fain would the officer have questioned the other three men who stood by the well but, at that moment, the Star appeared again in the East, and the whole caravan moved off, leaving Herod's officer no wiser than before.

The Problems

Perhaps you can determine which of the three men to whom he had been speaking was carrying the gold, which the frankincense, and which the myrrh. Moreover, which of them (if any) were truthful Wise Men, and which (if any) were lying servants?

And finally, if it be asked why Three Wise Men should engage three such dishonest servants, they did so in the knowledge that, by seeing the Holy Infant, these men would be reconciled to the truth. Indeed, after their visit to Bethlehem, no lie was ever again known to pass these servants' lips.

Lead p. 65
Solution p. 97

(40) CROSSNUMBER

A Crossnumber problem is similar to a Crossword problem with the difference that digits instead of letters must be entered in the lights (or spaces). The only restriction usually placed on these digits is that none of the numbers in the puzzle (reading either Across or Down) should begin with a zero, and this rule applies here. There is only one answer to the problem.

46

The Problems

ACROSS (ac.)

C. E *dn.*—M *ac.*

H. Difference between B *dn.* and M *dn.*

I. K *dn.* × 5

J. K *dn.* ÷ S *dn.*

K. O *ac.*³

M. E *dn.*—C *ac.*

N. $\sqrt{\text{N } dn.}$

O. $\sqrt[3]{\text{K } ac.}$

P. A multiple of I *dn.*

R. A palindromic number*

T. A *dn.* + B *dn.* + M *dn.*

U. L *dn.* ÷ 2

* A palindromic number is one that reads the same backwards as forwards (e.g. 12321)

DOWN (dn.)

A. A power of some number.

B. See H *ac.*

D. A number possessing a common factor with U *ac.*

E. C *ac.* + M *ac.*

F. The sum of the cubes of two consecutive numbers

G. The sum of the digits in Q *dn.*

I. A factor of P *ac.*

K. S *dn.* × J *ac.*

L. U *ac.* × 2

M. See H *ac.*

N. N *ac.*²

O. A multiple of U *ac.*

Q. See G *dn.*

S. K *dn.* ÷ J *ac.*

Lead   p. 65
Solution p. 98

(41)   PLEDGE'S LETTER

It all happened many years ago, and the outcome might have been very different had the letter not fallen into the hands of Mr. Pledge, an enthusiastic member of the M.C.C. At first he took the soiled and crumpled page to be the ravings of some lunatic, then it occurred to him that the letter could have some bearing on the death of the poor wretch who had been fished out of the Mudmarsh Canal earlier that morning. Pledge had found the letter on the towpath not far away. It could have come from the dead man's pocket.

He read it once again:

Sir,

Deal certain. Conditions. Attempt which for dark? Their of an too. As night to also on, but weather possible. In now.

The Problems

A craft the high watch, all with base figures. Land during A, as Will is their. They only command right.

May close; have need at plan. Keep morning—you it need Bill. Await they?

Kind regards to one and all.

Rex Portland

PS. Count on this; every word is on the square. You will have to get a move on, Sir, but be careful to check whenever need arises. Check again at the end, too. Then you must stop, because I have stopped in the wrong place.

Suddenly the whole idea became clear, and Mr. Pledge felt in his pocket for pencil and paper. For a few minutes he scribbled away, and then reached hurriedly for the telephone.

What was the message he had read?

Lead   **p. 65**
Solution p. 99

(42)   **CROW-FLIGHT**

While driving one blustery winter's day along the road which leads straight across the moors from Exetown to Wyeville, my friend stopped at a wayside petrol station. Noticing a road branching off to the left, he asked where it led.

'To Mainstead,' replied the attendant.

'Far from here?'

'As the crow flies, it is the same distance from here as we are from Exetown; that's exactly . . . (a violent gust of wind carried away his voice) . . . miles.'

'How far is Mainstead from Exetown, then?' asked my friend.

'As the crow flies, it's exactly . . . (another gust of wind) . . . miles. Same distance as it is from Wyeville—as the crow flies, that is.'

With further gusts of wind threatening to carry off even more crows, my friend desisted from his questioning, and resumed his journey to Wyeville which proved to be exactly eleven miles from the petrol station.

Assuming that when the attendant said 'exactly' he meant 'an exact number of miles', what was the distance of the petrol station from Mainstead—as the crow flies?

Lead   p. 65
Solution p. 100

(43)   BETTING TO WIN

Harbockle was a good mathematician but an unlucky gambler. On the five scheduled races of the day he lost just £120, and at that he would have had to be satisfied had the stewards not decided to add an 'Additional Race' to the programme.

Harbockle studied U. Backum's odds-board carefully before approaching the bookmaker to place his bets, for he was keen to make good his losses.

KNOW HOW	15 to 1
ACROSTIC	11 to 1
MY ZERO	8 to 1
EQUATION	7 to 1
ADVANTAGE	3 to 1
CALCULATION	2 to 1

'That is rather a lot of money,' remarked Mr. Backum after writing out Harbockle's betting tickets. 'Have you got it on you?'

'As a matter of fact, I have,' said Harbockle, 'but it would save you an awful lot of counting if you were just to hand me over £120 here and now; that's the amount I'm going to win.'

'But you don't know which horse is going to come home,' protested the bookmaker.

'Doesn't matter,' said Harbockle. 'I have placed my bets with you in such a way that I'm going to win that £120 whichever horse comes first.'

And Harbockle was right.

How much money did he lay on each horse?

Lead   p. 66
Solution p. 101

(44)   DIVIDE AND CONQUER

At the time of the Puzzoolian Conquest, Nosuchland was inhabited by four warring tribes known (from the patterns on their shields) as the Blackers, the Stipplers, the Hachures, and the Chequers. Each of these tribes occupied a block of five provinces from which they constantly made war, one upon the other.

In order to preserve peace, the Great Puzzooloo determined to scatter the tribes by re-allotting the provinces in such a way that each tribe should still be in possession of five provinces, but that no two adjoining provinces should be occupied by members of the same tribe. In this way he could prevent any tribe from mobilizing its forces.

Puzzooloo commenced by allocating the four central provinces in the manner shown on the map thus:

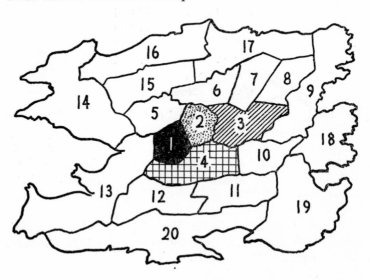

Now it was at this stage of the proceedings that Puzzooloo made his task far more difficult than it need have been. After the initial allocation of the four central provinces, there was still a great number of different ways in which the remainder of the provinces could have been distributed, but the very next allocation Puzzooloo made was province No. 16 to the Hachures, and this left only one possible way in which the remainder could be allocated.

Unfortunately before he had solved the problem all the tribes were once again at war. Can you discover the allocation that might have prevented this lamentable breach of the peace?

Lead   p. 66
Solution p. 102

(45)   CROWN AND ANCHOR

Three officers, so I am told, were sitting round the stove in Camp P.G. 29.

'It is a perfectly fair game,' said one. 'There is a green cloth divided into six squares marked with a Spade, a Heart, a Diamond, a Club, a Crown, and an Anchor.

'The players place their money on whichever square or squares they fancy, and the banker rolls out the dice—three of them—each marked with the same six symbols as those on the cloth. If, say, a Spade, a Heart, and an Anchor should turn up, the banker pays even money on all bets placed on those squares. Should two Clubs and a Crown turn up, the banker pays two-to-one on the Club bets, and even money on the Crown. In the event of, say, three Diamonds showing on the dice, he pays three to one on Diamonds.

The Problems

And, of course, in each case, losing bets are raked in by the bank. That seems fair enough to me.'

'Then why,' demanded the second officer, 'did that unshaven, bleary-eyed lance-corporal who used to run the Crown and Anchor school behind the cookhouse always wear such a self-satisfied smirk?'

'Perhaps,' suggested the third, 'it was because. . . .'

And thereat commenced an argument which seems to have been raging for quite a number of years. Do the odds in Crown and Anchor favour the bank and, if so, what proportion of the total moneys staked can the bank expect to win?

Lead   p. 66
Solution p. 103

(46)   CASTING UP

Hamlet, Othello, and *Macbeth* were the three plays chosen for the 1957 Shakespearean season at the Sphere Theatre, and seventy-five applications were received from actors hopeful of securing leading roles.

Those applicants who had never before played any of the parts were turned down by letter. The remainder, those who had played at least one of the roles, were all invited for interview, and in due course all presented themselves at the theatre. These experienced actors fell into two categories; those who had played only one of the three roles, and those who had played two of the three roles. None of them had played all three roles.

Now half of those who had played *Macbeth* had also played *Hamlet*; indeed, half of all the actors interviewed had played *Hamlet*. Those who had played *Othello* were three times the number of those who had played both *Hamlet* and *Macbeth*, but only a quarter of those who had played *Othello* had also played *Macbeth*. A certain number of the actors had played *Macbeth* only, and twice this number had played *Hamlet* only.

How many of the original applicants were turned down by letter because they had never before played any of the parts?

Lead   p. 66
Solution p. 104

The Problems

(47) CANNON-BALLS

'That big box over there without a top to it,' explained the castle guide, 'is the one in which they used to keep the cannon-balls. There was a gentleman in here only the other day measuring it up. He remarked on the fact that each of its sides, and its bottom too, is square, and that the box contains exactly the same number of cubic feet as there are square feet in its surface area—interior surface, that is.'

'How very interesting,' I remarked.

'Oh, that's not all,' went on the guide. 'The same gentleman measured up some of the old cannon-balls too, and he said that each cannon-ball contains exactly the same number of cubic inches as there are square inches on its surface. Now that is a coincidence for you, ain't it?'

'It is truly remarkable,' said I. 'He didn't say how many cannon-balls they were able to fit into the box, I suppose?'

'As a matter of fact, he didn't. He said I should be able to work that one out for myself, but I don't mind admitting it's a bit beyond me.'

Is it beyond you? In other words, what is the greatest number of cannon-balls that could be fitted into the box, provided they are stacked in such a way as to make the very best use of the space available? Remember that, although the box is without a top, no part of any ball is to protrude above the edge of the box.

Lead   p. 66
Solution p. 104

(48) GRAVE DIFFICULTIES

'Look at this infuriating instance of how moss and weather have conspired to obliterate essential details from a tombstone,' grumbled Professor Tree, the famous genealogist. He drew from his pocket a piece of paper on which was written:

Roger Galaday St. Semplice
Born Oct. 1, + + + + + + + + + +
Died Nov. 27, + + + + + + + + +
Aged 51 yrs.

Also his wife, Alice Mary
who survived him but 6 mths.
Born May 2, + + + + + + + +
Died May 27, + + + + + + +
Aged 36 yrs.

'I copied this only last week from a tombstone which is an important link in the history of the St. Semplice family, but all the Roman numerals representing the years have been eaten away by the ravages of time. One can still discern how many numerals were contained in each date, but the letters themselves are indecipherable. I have had to content myself with representing each numeral by a cross. And, of course, all I really want to know are the years of birth and death for the two persons mentioned.

'You being a bit of a mathematician, I was wondering if you could help me.'

(Just to refresh rusty, or moss-encrusted, memories, the Roman numerals are, I, V, X, L, C, D, M. E.g. 1794 would be written MDCCXCIV.)

Lead   p.   66
Solution p. 106

(49)   CLOSE FIT

In the small diagram shown here, the unit measurements of the five, small, rectangular pieces are:

V = 6 × 2,   W = 5 × 4,
X = 4 × 2,   Y = 5 × 2,
Z = 9 × 3. These dimensions are such that (as the diagram shows) the five pieces can be fitted together to form one large rectangle but, in every possible rectangular arrangement, the piece 'X'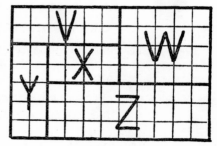

will always be completely surrounded by other pieces.

54

The Problems

By choosing our dimensions carefully it is possible to create other combinations with similar properties. For instance, the eleven rectangular pieces shown below can also be fitted together to form one large rectangle.

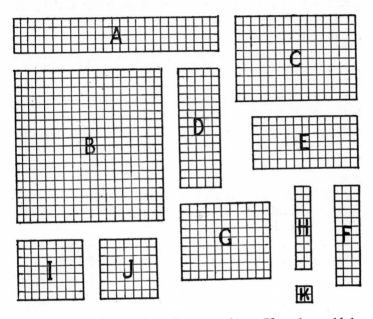

If this were done, what piece, or pieces (if any) would be completely surrounded?

Luck and patience may enable you to solve the problem by trial and error, but logical analysis should make the task much easier.

Lead   p. 67
Solution p. 107

(50)   AN 'INSOLUBLE' PROBLEM

Colonel Factor's regiment consisted entirely of officers, sergeants, and privates. Each of the colonel's officers had under his command an equal number of sergeants, and, in turn, each sergeant commanded an equal number of privates—of course there were more privates than sergeants, and more sergeants than officers.

In this way all the personnel of the regiment were accounted for. There was, however, a general Army order limiting the number of privates that could be placed under a sergeant's command, and this order had been strictly adhered to.

The total number of privates in the colonel's regiment was 294. How many officers were there (excluding the colonel himself) and how many sergeants?

Now I know that the problem as it stands is quite insoluble; in fact, it would still be insoluble even if I were to tell you how many persons there were in the regiment altogether—though if I were then to tell you the maximum number of privates that could be placed under a sergeant's command, the questions could be answered.

As it is, I am going to tell you neither of these things. Nevertheless you should be able to solve the problem, for you now have all the information necessary for so doing.

Incidentally, what was the maximum number of privates permitted to be placed under a sergeant's command?

Lead   p. 67
Solution p. 108

Leads

The purpose of this section is to provide the reader with certain hints and clues that may assist him in solving a problem which he finds to be too abstruse in its originally stated form.

Readers who have solved a problem are also advised to refer to the Lead before verifying their answer in the Solutions at the back of the book. In some instances the Lead indicates what is NOT the answer to a particular problem and if, perchance, the reader discovers that he has arrived at one of these wrong answers, he can then go back and recheck his reasoning in an attempt to find the true answer before turning up the solution.

LEADS

(1) **Zoologistics.** Assign a letter to each of the statements thus: JABBERWOCK lives (A) in a Tumtum Tree, or (B) in the Wabe. BANDERSNATCH is (C) a bird, or (D) an animal. JUBJUB has (E) 5 wings, or (F) 4 wings, and eats (G) Raths, or (H) Toves, or (J) Borogoves. Then the various statements were:

ALICE	B	C	F	J
MAD HATTER	A	D	E	H
MARCH HARE	A	C	F	H
DORMOUSE	A	C	E	G

If, say, A and C were true statements, what could be said of the other entries in the table? What other possible true pairs are there?

(2) **Spinning Wheel.** Add together each pair of opposite numbers on the disc. What have all these pairs in common? What must the scores of each pair of opposite boys have totalled, each spin? Who had the lowest total, and what is the most he could possibly have scored?

(3) **Coupling.** Which two of the men could not possibly have been the 'son' referred to? Could Charles have been married to Ethel? Had Charles been married to Frieda, who must have been the mother of the 'son'? Who then would have been her daughter?

(4) **The Plantation.** Plot out small fields surrounded by, say, 8, 12, 16 . . . etc. men (or dots). What is the relationship in each case between the number of men and the unit area they enclose?

(5) **Uneven Odds.** In how many ways is it possible to throw 12, 11, 10 . . . etc., with two dice? In how many ways, then, can one throw 6 or more? (*The answer to the problem is not* 17s. 6d.)

(6) **Conundra Zoo.** It is no good merely moving an animal into his own proper cage at the earliest possible moment; he will only

Leads

block the way of others later on. The important thing is to shepherd the animals into their right *cyclic* order. (*If you have taken more than 16 moves, try again.*)

(7) **Full Marks.** What subjects did Mabel pass in? Was she a twin? When did John finish? In what subjects could he not have got full marks? In what order were girls and boys seated? Remember, only one child cheated.

(8) **Venusian Feelers.** Whatever number Venusians may count up to before they reach double figures, could $2 + 3$ ever equal more than 5 (i.e. could they ever equal, say, 15 or 25)? What is $4 + 5$ in earthly figures? What do the Venusians call this quantity?

(9) **Holiday Plans.** Do you think the answer to this problem could possibly be fair? Now think!

(10) **Changing Ways.** If you were to have a shilling, a sixpence, and a threepence, in how many ways could you make up the remaining 1d.? In how many ways could the remaining pence be made up if you were to leave out the threepence . . . the sixpence . . . the shilling?

(11) **Python Gorge.** The claim has obviously to be $\sqrt{3}$ chains long on each side, so this distance must somehow be marked out. If the prospector remembered the Pyth(ag)o(rea)n principle, $h^2 = \sqrt{a^2 + b^2}$, how many lengths of rope (or fractions of a length) should he choose for a and b respectively, in order to make $h = \sqrt{3}$? How should he now incorporate this length in his square?

(12) **Money for Jam.** The total number of jars must be a multiple of what number? If certain of the competitors got exactly two-thirds right, but failed to exceed Mr. Wattsitt's 17, what is the maximum possible number of jars? If Mr. Wattsitt got 17 right, there must have been *at least* how many jars? Be very careful here.

(13) **Piper's Tank.** 'Of all the *solid*, geometrical, rectangular

figures, the cube contains the greatest volume in proportion to its surface area.' Perhaps you can go on from there. (*The answer is not 428 gallons.*)

(14) **The Lost Code.** 'x' and 'T' stand in the message as full words. What are the only two English words they could represent? What possible words, then, could 'TXS' represent? How would possible equivalents for 's' then fit into 'vss'? Now compare 'TRIKE' and 'STRIKE'.

(15) **Figure it Out.** (i) Look at the last column, $X + X + X = ?X$. What digit when multiplied by 3 will reproduce itself in the answer? (ii) The fourth line has only three figures in it. H can therefore be no more than . . . ? Could H be 1? Could it be 3? (iii) The remainder NKN must be less than the divisor WJD. What can therefore be said about N and W? Now look at the column $K - S = Y$, $Y - D = K$. Has anything been 'carried' to these subtractions? If not, what must be the value of $S + D$?

(16) **Colour Combinations.** Letter the sides of the cube A to F. In how many ways can A be painted? For each of these ways, how many ways are there of painting B . . . and so on? How many identical sides has a cube? In how many ways may each side be presented to you? (*The answer to the cube is not 720. The answer to the tetrahedron is not 24, nor is it 6.*)

(17) **Tiddlywinks.** What *must* Round 1 Mat 4 be? Could Round 3 Mat 1 be Cb? How many terms like Aa, Ab, Ac . . . can there be? Try numbering them 1, 2, 3, . . . etc. Then what sorts of numbers must appear in the same row or in the same column of the table?

(18) **Crown, Orb, and Sceptre.** If the age order of the sons had been AFJ, how many chests would originally have gone to the children? How many if the order had been AJF, FAJ, . . . etc.? If one child dies in any of these combinations, what is the *minimum* number of chests that must still go to children? What if the king had 2 . . . 3 . . . 4 daughters?

Leads

(19) Pastry-Cutter. With three cuts you *must* produce at least 4 pieces. Can you produce 5 . . . 6? (*If you have finished up with less than 45 pieces in all, try again.*)

(20) Share Prices. How many O.B.T.s and Addingtons were finally bought? Call the price of an O.B.T. £x, of a Geomercantile £y, and of an Addington £z. Then $105x + 75y + 30z = 100$. What other two equations can be derived from the story?

(21) Digital Wanderers. What amount must the boys' donation exceed if the total is to be kept below £1m.? What amounts between this figure and £1 are divisible by 11? Now for the pounds —here is a rule to help you: *In order for a number to be divisible by 11, either the sum of its digits in the odd places must equal the sum of its digits in the even places, or the difference between these two sums must be 11 or a multiple of 11.*

(22) Calculari's Concerts. Which composers were played in every concert? Which concerts started with Liszt? Which are the only places Mozart and Chopin can occupy in a concert? Which places Beethoven and Chopin?

(23) A Safe Number. Let us suppose the last digit of Quaddle's number happened to be 8. Then the required number would be of the form of:

$$\begin{array}{r} \text{abcd}\ldots\ldots\text{efgh8} \\ \times\,8 \\ \hline \text{8abcd}\ldots\ldots\text{efgh} \end{array}$$

How many digits must be inserted to produce a sum of this form? Try working it out. How many sums like the above can be devised?

(24) Court Cards. To transfer a stack containing only 1 card would obviously require only 1 move. How many moves for 2 . . . 3 . . . 4, etc.? Is there any mathematical relationship between the numbers so obtained? (*If your Court Cards take more than 31 moves, or your Piquet suit more than 255, try again.*)

Leads

(25) **Long Division.** It is true that a number divisible by two different numbers is not *necessarily* divisible by the product of those numbers but (although mathematical textbooks seem reluctant to mention the fact) it can be shown that: *If a number is divisible by two numbers that are mutually prime* (i.e. have no common divisor but 1) *the number is also divisible by the product of those two numbers.* Remember also these two rules: *If the sum of the digits in a number is divisible by 9, the number itself is divisible by 9,* and *If the last three digits of a number are divisible by 8, the number itself is divisible by 8.*

(26) **Riddleton By-Election.** How many votes did the third candidate receive in the 1955 election? At that election, Labour got two-fifths of the vote, and the Conservative 4,997 more than this. How many voted altogether at that election? How many at the by-election? Mr. Freer's votes must have been a multiple of what number?

(27) **A Matter of X-ercise.** Can we say that A to B (at horse speed) + C to A (at bike speed) equals in time A to B (at bike speed) + C to A (at horse speed)? What considerations could make this possible? (*The answer is not 18 miles.*)

(28) **Rookery.** How many routes are there to *any* square in the top row . . . to *any* square in the left-hand column? How many routes to the second . . . third . . . etc. square in the second row? What *two* numbers make up the total of any such routes?

(29) **Pin-Pointing Sabotage.** The pin would have followed a path known geometrically as a cycloid,

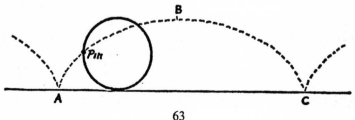

Leads

Now the length of a full cycloid arch from A to C is *exactly* four times the diameter of the circle that generates it. Moreover, the two halves of the arch (A to B, and B to C) are symmetrical.

(30) **Pip Poker.** How many pips were held by each child? How could the Sixes have been distributed . . . the Fives?

(31) **Running to Time.** Do *not* try to work out the area of the small field; you need not know it. In unresolved terms one side of the property is $\sqrt{2}$ miles long. How long, in unresolved terms, is one side of the small field? Call the distance walked by the farmer M miles, the distance run by Tom D miles. In these terms, how far had the farmer walked, and how far had Tom run when the boy caught up with his father?

(32) **Checking Precedent.** Try solving the problem with a smaller number of pieces. (*If you have taken more than 70 moves, try again.*)

(33) **Barber's Pole.** The reference to π is merely a bit of leg-pulling. π does not come into the problem. Imagine the pole were not solid, but a cylinder that could be split down the centre, and rolled flat. What then?

(34) **Noughts and Crosses.** Assume 'Cross' starts the play, then a legitimate game could finish up showing 3 Xs and 2 Os, 3 Xs and 3 Os . . . etc. How many such combinations can there be? How many diagrams would be needed for each such combination? (*The answer is not 1840; remember those 'certain rare types of legitimate wins'.*)

(35) **Multiple Motors.** The total value of all cars *sold* must be divisible by what small number? What car must be excluded from the list to make the value of the remainder divisible by this number? Could the Straitley have been sold in the morning?

(36) **Circle of Fate.** If you despise mere trial and error, try working

out the position in which Algebar would have to stand in a ring of 3, 4, 5, . . . etc. men in order to be the last left. Compare the number of men in each such ring with the position he must occupy in that ring.

(37) **A Piece of Cake.** The side of each small cake must be $1/\sqrt{5}$ of the side of the large one. Is there any way in which you can establish this distance? (*If you have more than 9 pieces try again.*)

(38) **Extensive Reasoning.** Join A to C, and E to G. The total area AEFGC can now be made up in two different ways. What can you deduce from the common elements in these two ways? (*If your answer has any shillings or pence in it, it is wrong.*)

(39) **Gifts of the Magi.** Tabulate all the ways in which the gifts could have been carried by Gaspar, Melchior, and Balthazar respectively, e.g. G(old) M(yrrh) F(rankincense), G.F.M., F.G.M. etc. Apply the statements to each. For instance, in the case of G.M.F. is Balthazar truthful or not? How would his truthfulness or otherwise affect the legitimacy of Melchior's statements?

(40) **Crossnumber.** Consider N *dn* = N *ac*². What is the only digit that can then go in the N square? Is the second figure in L *dn* odd or even? Can the figure in the U square be more than 5? Considering the last digit of K *ac* what two values might suit O *ac*? This is the sort of reasoning you should try to employ.

(41) **Pledge's Letter.** What could be the literal meaning of 'every word is on the square'? On what sort of squares is it possible to 'check'? Who would be addressed as 'Sir', and what does 'Rex' stand for? In what directions must 'Sir' 'get a move on'? What words might he pass on the way?

(42) **Crow Flight.** Construct a diagram. Join M to O (the middle point of XY). Let XP = *a*, MX = *b*, MO = *c*. What does MP equal? What are the *algebraic* lengths of XO and OP? Calculate the algebraic lengths of *c* and *b*. What is b^2? In the expression for

b^2 there should be a number which itself is equal to two consecutive numbers. What is the significance of these two consecutive numbers?

(43) Betting to Win. If there were only two horses in a race, one quoted at 5 to 1, and the other at 2 to 1, and if you were to put £2 on the first and £4 on the second, how much would you be sure of winning? Why?

(44) Divide and Conquer. There is no mathematical short cut to the solution of this problem, but certain types of observations may help you. For instance, 14, 15, and 17 must all be different races. How is 17 affected by allocating 5 to the Chequers or, alternatively, to the Hachures? Such is the sort of reasoning you should use.

(45) Crown and Anchor. Firstly, the bank *does* stand to win. Imagine that there is 1/– on each square, each throw. Which sorts of throw benefit the banker, and by how much? Tabulate all the possible ways in which the three dice may fall. What does such a table tell you? (*If your answer to the problem is one twenty-seventh, check again your ways of throwing three dice.*)

(46) Casting Up. Try to work out what *proportion* of the total number interviewed had played only *Othello*. Having done that, remember that the producer had no intention of playing Shylock.

(47) Cannon-Balls. The total area of the box will be $5s^2$, and its volume s^3. From this you can establish the exact size of the box in feet. Similarly from the formulae: Area $= d^2\pi$, and Volume $= \dfrac{d^3\pi}{6}$ you can establish the exact size of a cannon-ball in inches. Stacking the balls calls for much ingenuity. (*The answer is not 1,000, nor 1186. It is possible to do better than that.*)

(48) Grave Difficulties. Alice died in the year following Roger's death. How does this addition of 1 affect the number of letters in the dates? What, therefore, must be the last four letters in Roger's death-date? Discover the other letters by working from right to left.

(49) Close Fit. What is the total area of the eleven pieces? What then are the only possible dimensions of the rectangle (remembering that B must be accommodated)? Mark out the area of the rectangle and place A on it. If A were to lie breadthwise (as distinct from lengthwise), could any piece fill the gap (or gaps) at its end (or ends)? Now add B and C to the area. Next add E, and then G, F, J, D, K, I, H (preferably in that order).

(50) An 'Insoluble' Problem. What are the prime factors of 294? How can these be combined to represent (*a*) number of officers, (*b*) number of sergeants under each officer, (*c*) number of privates under each sergeant? Which of these combinations would *not* (even if you knew how many people were in the regiment) enable you to answer the question? How many privates are under each sergeant in these indeterminate combinations?

Solutions

Facts and formulae already provided in the Leads Section are not normally repeated in the Solutions, which usually follow the line of argument suggested by the Leads.

Although none of the problems has more than one correct solution, that solution can sometimes be obtained in a variety of ways. The ways described in the following pages have been chosen with the idea of revealing as many as possible of the basic principles underlying the problems. In some instances the solver may have employed quite different methods that are equally valid. Whatever methods are used, however, the actual answer arrived at should be the same as that given in the first paragraph of the solution.

SOLUTIONS

(1)   **Zoologistics**

The Jabberwock lives in the Wabe. The Bandersnatch is a bird. The Jubjub has five wings and feeds on Toves.

Consider the table suggested in the Lead. Since each member of the party has only two true statements, the only possible pairs of true statements for, say, the Dormouse are AC, AE, AG, CE, CG, or EG.

If A and C are both true, then B and D are both false (for A is inconsistent with B, and C with D). Also E and G are false (because the Dormouse has only two true statements). Again, F and H are false (because the March Hare has only two true statements). Then the Mad Hatter would have three false statements (D, E, and H) which is impossible. Therefore A and C do not constitute a pair of true statements.

Similarly it may be shown that AE, AG, CG, and EG are impossible combinations for true statements. Therefore, in the case of the Dormouse, the only possible pair of true statements is the remaining pair, CE. The rest follows quite easily.

(2)   **Spinning Wheel**

Arthur 15, Barry 14, Charles 13, David 10, Ernest 11, Frank 12. Each pair of opposite numbers on the disc totals 5. Each pair of opposite boys must therefore have scored a total of 5 each spin, i.e. 25 for all 5 spins—no more and no less! If Arthur finished with the highest total then it follows that David finished with the lowest.

The lowest scorer (David) could not have made more than 11, for had he scored 12, Arthur would have scored only 13 and could not possibly have been the clear winner.

The disposal of the numbers on the disc is such that David could have taken the lead on the second spin only by obtaining a 5, giving him a progressive total of 9. Then, since 11 is his possible maximum, at least one of the remaining spins must have resulted in his getting a 0. Three spins have therefore been uniquely

Solutions

determined, for which three spins it may easily be worked out that the boys had progressive totals of A = 6, B = 7, C = 10, D = 9, E = 8, F = 5. For the remaining two spins, David's scores could have been 0–0, 0–1, 1–1, or 0–2, but the first and last of these would then result in Arthur tying with someone else instead of winning. Again, 1–1 for David would give two fives to Frank making Frank the winner. In the remaining two spins David therefore scored 0–1.

All five positions of the disc are now uniquely determined, and from these positions the scores of each player may simply be added up.

(3)   **Coupling**

Algernon was married to Frieda, Bertrand to Ethel, and Charles to Doris. Charles and Ethel were the son and daughter of Algernon and his wife.

Since Algernon's father was dead, and Bertrand the oldest person, neither of these could have been the son referred to. The son must therefore have been Charles, who could not have been married to Ethel (for she was talking to Charles's wife).

Now had Charles been married to Frieda, one of the other men must have been married to Ethel (who had no son) and the third to Doris who, in this case, would have been Charles's mother. But if Doris were the 'mother' her daughter could have been only Frieda—not Ethel (for Doris and Ethel were the same age). This would mean that Charles had married his sister which, under English law at least, is quite illegal. Charles then must have been married to Doris.

With Charles married to Doris, Algernon could not have been married to Ethel (a woman of Doris's age) for Algernon's wife was older than Charles's. Therefore Algernon was the husband of Frieda and their children were Charles and Ethel (not Charles and Doris, for that too would have meant brother marrying sister). Bertrand is then left with Ethel (which means that Bertrand is older than his father-in-law; but there is nothing illegal about that, even though some unkind persons might suspect that Ethel married for money).

72

Solutions

The Plantation

There were 160 acres in the field.

In such an array, the unit area of the field is always the square of quarter the number of men. Therefore if the number of men is x, and the distance between them is 22 yards, they will enclose an area of $(22x \div 4)^2$ square yards. But x men also enclose x acres in our problem, i.e. 4,840x square yards. Therefore $\left(\dfrac{22x}{4}\right)^2 = 4840x$. That is, $121x = 19{,}360$. Therefore $x = 160$ which is the number of men and also the number of acres in the field.

(With each man standing 22 yards apart, there would be too few men per acre if the field were any larger, and too many per acre if the field were any smaller.)

(5) **Uneven Odds**

Against Blithering's 10s., Henshaw should have been prepared to wager 26s.

When this problem was first published, many solvers suggested 17s. 6d., reasoning no doubt that, since Henshaw could have thrown only four numbers less than six (2, 3, 4, 5) but seven equal to or greater than six (6, 7, 8, 9, 10, 11, 12), the odds should be in the proportion of 4 : 7. But even these odds give Henshaw an outrageous advantage.

The true reasoning is this. Since each side of each die may be matched with each side of the other die, there are $6 \times 6 = 36$ different ways in which they may be combined. Now there is only 1 way of throwing Two, 2 ways of throwing Three, 3 ways of throwing Four, and 4 ways of throwing Five; i.e. $1 + 2 + 3 + 4 = 10$ ways of throwing less than Six, leaving 26 ways of throwing Six or more. The odds must therefore, if they are to be fair, be in the proportion of 26 : 10. (Notice that a 1 on Die 'A' plus a 2 on Die 'B' constitutes quite a separate chance from that of a 2 on Die 'A' plus a 1 on Die 'B'. This is a very important point to remember in dice problems.)

Solutions

In full the moves are: Rhino to enclosure, Gorilla to bear's cage, Tiger to rhino's cage, Rhino to lion's cage, Gorilla to enclosure, Lion to bear's cage, Bear to gorilla's cage, Gorilla to tiger's cage, Lion to enclosure, Tiger to bear's cage, Rhino to rhino's cage, Lion to lion's cage, Tiger to enclosure, Bear to bear's cage, Gorilla to gorilla's cage, Tiger to tiger's cage. Sixteen moves in all. There is no other sequence of moves which will achieve the object so economically.

Notice that the moves fall into four successive cycles of four moves each, one cycle to get each animal into his proper cyclic order relative to one other animal.

Betty got full marks in Arithmetic, John in History, Mabel in English, and Tom in Geography. And John cheated.

Since Mabel passed in all subjects she was not a twin, and must therefore have been (at least) third to finish, and John must have been last. The twins were therefore Betty and Tom, and it must have been Betty (using a pencil) who got full marks in Arithmetic. Therefore John could not have got full marks in Arithmetic. Moreover, being last to finish, he failed in Geography and could not therefore have got full marks in English either. History was therefore the subject in which he got full marks.

Since we now know that one twin was a boy and the other a girl, and since they were separated by one other child, and since the girls were not seated together, the children can only have been sitting thus: Girl - Boy - Boy - Girl. John must have therefore cribbed to find the answer to the first History question (without which he could not have gained full marks in that subject) for only those at opposite ends of the desk (i.e. the two girls) knew the answer to this question.

Since these same two girls were stumped by a Geography question, Mabel could not have got full marks in Geography (only one child cheated). She therefore got full marks in English, and Tom must have got full marks in the remaining subject, Geography.

74

Solutions

Venusian Feelers

The Venusian (in earth figures) had 68 children (31 sons and 37 daughters)—and 7 feelers.

$2 + 3$ could not equal more than simply 5 in any scale, therefore nothing is carried over into the Venusian addition of $4 + 5 = 12$. Now $4 + 5$ in our figures means 9, a quantity that, as we have seen, the Venusian expressed by a 1 and a 2. When we say 12, the 1 represents 10 (the number of fingers we possess) and the 2 represents what is to be added. Similarly, when the Venusian says 12, the 1 represents the number of feelers he possesses, plus 2, and this is the quantity we call 9. Obviously then he must have 7 feelers.

Then when he says 'I have 43 sons' he means that he has four times the number of feelers on his head plus 3 sons, which is $4 \times 7 + 3 = 31$. Similarly he has $5 \times 7 + 2 = 37$ daughters.

Mathematically the problem could be tackled by solving the equation: $(4R + 3) + (5R + 2) = R^2 + 2R + 5$, where R represents the radix of the scale being sought.

(9) **Holiday Plans**

Yes, the answer *is* fair. Fair Isle (in the Shetlands).

Uncle Cryptopher's remarks are all equivoques based on homonymous and homophonous equivalents of the word FAIR.

If the story be re-read with the solution in mind, the allusions should be fairly obvious. 'Just' (in the sense of equitable), 'beautiful', 'fine and sunny', 'blonde', 'so-so', 'not that good', and 'honest' are all synonyms of FAIR. The 'big sell' refers to the country market which is usually very popular with children. 'Pulling wool over one's eyes' is just what one would have to do if donning a Fair-Isle, which is a sort of sweater.

If the island, FAIR, were to have a 'way' with it, we should get a FAIRWAY that should attract golfers. Again the island provides a small article (the indefinite article 'a') in wood ('fir') as can be seen in F(A)IR.

The 'sound' of FAIR is identical with that of its homophone, FARE (meaning food). Similarly, 'Just say the word' is an enjoinder to pronounce the word FAIR to get another homophone, FARE (meaning passage money).

Solutions

(10)   **Changing Ways**

(*a*) 223 ways. (*b*) 188 ways.

Usually such problems can best be solved by orderly tabulation;
e.g:

1/–	6d.	3d.	1d.	Cases
1	1	1	1—0	2
1	1	0	4—0	5
1	0	3	1—0	2
1	0	2	4—0	5
1	0	1	7—0	8
1	0	0	10—0	11
0	3	1	1—0	2
0	3	0	4—0	5
0	2	3	1—0	2
0	2	2	4—0	5

and so on.

The first line means that one possible combination is a shilling,
a sixpence, and a threepence, leaving the sum of 1d. to be made
up in copper. Obviously this can be done by using either 1 penny
or no pennies (i.e. halfpennies instead of pennies)—a total of
2 cases. Similarly the second line may require 4, 3, 2, 1, or 0
pennies (again the balance in each case being made up of halfpennies)—a total of 5 cases. If this table is extended to 26 lines
in all, 223 cases will be accounted for. It will also be apparent from
the table that lines 17, 18, 23, 24, 25, and 26 (representing a total
of 105 cases) would contravene the legal tender condition.

(11)   **Python Gorge**

The problem is essentially one of constructing a right angle, and
then building on it a square of side $\sqrt{3}$ chains. The following
construction achieves both aims simultaneously, and is probably
the most geometrically elegant of several alternatives. The construction also eliminates the practical problem of pinning a rope
at its very extremity.

76

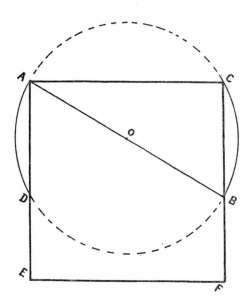

Halve the rope. Insert a peg through the strands at the centre point, and drive in this peg at O. Stretch one end of the rope and peg A at a distance of 1 chain. Similarly peg B, aligning B with A and O by sighting. With the half-rope swinging round O, scratch out a circle (or just the two arcs as shown). With the rope-centre pinned at B, mark and peg the point C on the circle. Similarly, from A, mark and peg D. Remove the peg from the rope. Pin the rope near one of its ends to A, stretch to C, and mark the distance AC along the rope (by knotting or holding the rope at that point). Swing the rope round and peg E so that AE =AC (aligning E with D and A by sighting). Similarly with the rope pinned at C, make CF = AC. The pegs, A, C, E, F, now indicate the required square.

Since ABC is inscribed in a semicircle, it is a right-angled triangle. Therefore, since AB = 2 chains and CB = 1 chain, $AC = \sqrt{2^2 - 1^2} = \sqrt{3}$.

Solutions

Money for Jam

It would have been much fairer to have shared the second prize of £50 between all the 4,960 people who got sixteen right, and not merely between a 'lucky' sixty of them. The recipients might have been disappointed with the size of their winnings, but at least they would have got back nearly the cost of posting their entries.

The whole point of the problem is that there must have been 24 jars pictured in the contest, and two-thirds of 24 is 16.

Some competitors got exactly half right, and others exactly two-thirds. The number of jars must therefore have been a multiple of 6, e.g. 18, 24, 30, . . . etc. However the number could not have been 18, for then Mr. Wattsitt could not have got only 17; with 18 jars and 18 labels, if 17 of them are matched up correctly, the remaining jar and label must themselves form a correctly matched pair. Again, had the number of jars been 30 (or any greater multiple of 6) competitors getting two-thirds right would have scored more than the winner himself.

(13) **Piper's Tank**

474 gallons is the maximum capacity obtainable.

From the rule given in the Lead, it follows that, if a hollow cube were to be sliced in half we should obtain two rectilinear figures (each without a top) each of which would contain the greatest possible volume for its surface area. This, then, is the sort of figure we are looking for.

Now since the height of such a figure will be half its length, its square base will account for one-third of its total area which is $85\frac{1}{3}$ sq. ft. The base must therefore be given an area of $28\frac{4}{9}$ sq. ft., the square root of which is $5\frac{1}{3}$ ft. The four sides must then be $5\frac{1}{3}$ ft. by $2\frac{2}{3}$ ft. There are several quite simple ways of dissecting the rectangle into pieces of these dimensions.

The capacity of the tank will then be $5\frac{1}{3} \times 5\frac{1}{3} \times 2\frac{2}{3} \times 6\frac{1}{4} = 474$ (to the nearest gallon).

(14) **The Lost Code**

The message reads: *Dozens of odd rumours reaching us suggest anger is quickening. In my view danger spots are Bombaz and Lam-baza. I must have a bit of aid up here by next January.*

                                                                    Henshaw

'I' and 'a' are the only two single-letter words in the language, therefore 'x' and 'T' must each be one of these. 'TXS' must there-fore be either 'ia?' or 'ai?'. The word could therefore be 'Ian', 'ail', 'aim', 'air', or 'aid', assuming 's' to be either 'n', 'l', 'm', 'r' or 'd' respectively. But should 's' represent any of the first four of these letters, 'vss' would be meaningless ('v' cannot be 'a' or 'i', which letters have already been assigned to 'x' or 'T'). Admittedly 'vss' could be 'ell', but this would make 'vQ TXS' read 'e? ail', a meaningless combination. 'TXS' can therefore only be 'aid', and 'vss' only 'odd'.

Now compare 'TRIKE' and 'STRIKE' (which latter word we now know to be 'da????'). The only six-letter words starting with 'da' and still meaning something if their first letter is omitted are 'dangle' and 'danger', but 'STRIKE' cannot be 'dangle' for that would make 'E' to be 'e', making 'TEK' to be 'ae?'. 'STRIKE' is therefore 'danger', and we have now discovered 'a(T), i(X), d(S), o(V), n(R), g(I), e(K), r(E)'.

Similarly we may decipher 's(F), u(P), j(B), y(C), m(Z), b(G), p(H), t(A), f(Q), z(M), h(N), c(Y), k(W), q(U), x(L), v(J), w(O).' With twenty-five pairs thus accounted for, the remaining 'l' and 'D' must form the twenty-sixth pair.

(15)   **Figure It Out**

(i) $X = 5$, $B = 6$, $R = 3$, $T = 9$. (ii) $H = 2$, $Z = 5$, $C = 6$, $P = 3$, $Q = 4$, $L = 7$, $F = 9$, $M = 1$, $A = 8$. (iii) $N = 1$, $W = 2$, $S = 3$, $D = 7$, $J = 5$, $K = 9$, $V = 0$, $G = 4$, $Y = 6$.

(i) In the last column, the only digit that will reproduce itself in the answer is 5 (0 would also, but in the first line this would be absurd, the first 0 being redundant). If X is 5, B can only be 6. In the second last column, $B(6) + R + 1$ (carried forward) must equal 10, for T to reappear in the answer. $\therefore$ R is 3. Similarly, in the second column, T must be 9.

(ii) H is less than 4, otherwise the fourth line would run into four figures. It cannot be 3, for then Z could only be 9, and the fifth line would run into five figures. It cannot be 1, for then the fourth line would be HLP, ∴ H is 2. ∴ Z is 4 or 5, and C (below it) is 5 or 6. But C (notice H(2) × P = ?C) must be even. ∴ C is 6, and Z is 5. ∴ P (notice H(2) × P = ?6) is 3 or 8. But P × H is less than 10 (to produce only three figures in the third line). ∴ P is 3. Now A can only be 7 or 8. ∴ Q must be 3, 4, or 5. But Q must also be even. ∴ Q is 4. Divide H(2) into Z(5)Q(4)C(6) to find HLP and L becomes 7. The rest follows by simple multiplication.

(iii) Since WJD is the divisor, and NKN the remainder, N must be less than W. ∴ the subtraction of D from Y is unaffected by 'borrowing' and the whole column KSYDK represents a straightforward double subtraction in which the two subtractors S and D must together equal 10 in order that K shall reappear in the last line. The only combinations that equal 10 are 1 and 9, 2 and 8, 3 and 7, 4 and 6, 5 and 5. 5 and 5 is inapplicable because S and D are different. 4 × 6 would produce 24, and therefore could not apply to the operation S × D = ??N, because N could not be 4 if either S or D were already 4. A similar argument applies to 1 and 9. 2 and 8 would result in the second D of DDN being an odd number which, by postulation of D as 2 or 8, is absurd. ∴ S and D are either 3 and 7 or 7 and 3. In either case, N must be 1, and ∴ (see last column) W is 2. S cannot be 7, otherwise S × W(2)JD would result in the second last line running into four figures. ∴ S is 3 and D must be 7. Dividing S(3) into D(7)D(7)N(1), WJD becomes 257, J being 5. Now K × D(7) = ?S(3). ∴ K can only be 9. Now S being less than K, V – N(1) = K(9) is a straight subtraction in which V must be 0. S must, therefore, be increased by a borrowed 1 in the subtraction G – S(3) = 0, i.e. G – 4 = 0. G then is 4. Y is 6, by simple subtraction.

(16)   **Colour Combinations**

There are thirty essentially different ways of colouring a cube (the same number as for a pyramid). There are only two essentially different ways of colouring an equilateral tetrahedron.

The last answer is surprising because one may be tempted to reason thus: 'If I paint side A green, there are three ways in which

Solutions

I may paint side B; so even ignoring the other two sides there are at least three different ways of colouring the tetrahedron.' The fallacy lies in the fact that, whatever colour one chooses for side B, the choice automatically determines the cyclic colour relationship between either A and C, or A and D.

The true reasoning for the tetrahedron is this: There are 4 ways of painting A, for each of which there are 3 ways of painting B, for each of which there are 2 ways of painting C, for each of which there is only 1 way of painting D. Therefore there are $4 \times 3 \times 2 \times 1 = 24$ ways of painting the tetrahedron—BUT, since there are four *identically disposed* sides only a quarter of this number (i.e. 6) may be essentially different. But each side may also be based in three different ways, therefore only one third of 6 (i.e. 2) will give rise to essentially different cyclic permutations.

On this reasoning we may construct a general formula for the colouring of all *regular* polyhedra: $\dfrac{F!}{F \times e}$ where F = the number of faces, and e the number of edges to *each face*. Thus for the cube $\dfrac{6!}{6 \times 4} = \dfrac{6 \times 5 \times 4 \times 3 \times 2 \times 1}{6 \times 4} = 30$.

(17) **Tiddlywinks**

	Mat 1	Mat 2	Mat 3	Mat 4
Round 1	Aa	Bb	Cc	**Dd**
Round 2	Bc	Ad	Da	Cb
Round 3	**Cd**	Dc	Ab	Ba
Round 4	**Db**	Ca	Bd	Ac

The terms in bold type are immediately deducible. To the sixteen terms Aa, Ab, Ac, Ad, Ba, Bb, . . . etc. allocate the numbers 1–16 and set them down in square form thus:

(1)	2	3	4
5	(6)	(7)	8
9	10	(11)	(12)
13	(14)	15	(16)

If we now write into our partly completed table the terms already decided (bracketing or otherwise cancelling the numbers, as above, as we proceed) we can complete the table by selecting from our square in such a way that each number for every Round must come from both a different column and a different row of the square. Thus, Round 2 can contain only 13, 10, 4 (in some order) in addition to its 7, and Mat 2 can contain only 15, 9, 4 (in some order) in addition to its 6. 4, the only number appearing in both these selections, must therefore be entered for Round 2 Mat 2, and so on.

If the table is completed in this manner, and the numbers then replaced by their corresponding terms, Aa, Ab, etc., the solution will be complete. Incidentally, your numerical table will be a semi-magic square in which each row and each column will total 34. Three-dimensional permutations such as are implied by this problem can often be reduced to Magic Squares. The problem illustrates the importance of assigning to data terms that are easily handled.

(18)   **Crown, Orb, and Sceptre**

Albert received the Crown, Joseph the Orb, and Ferdinand the Sceptre.

Had the age order of the sons been AFJ, the total number of chests originally intended for the families would have been 16; if AJF 17, FAJ 17, FJA 19, JAF 19, JFA 20. But some chests were reserved for the king's daughters, so we must eliminate FJA, JAF, JFA.

Thus the king had 3 daughters (assigned 1 chest each), 2 daughters (2 chests each), or 4 daughters (1 chest each).

If 2 or 4 daughters, the age order of the sons must have been AFJ, but with 4 daughters receiving 1 *extra* chest each, the number remaining for the sons' families would be reduced to 12, whereas at least 13 are necessary, irrespective of whose child dies. Two daughters receiving 1 extra chest each would leave 14 for the families, but this would tally only if Ferdinand's child died, but he had no son. Therefore we must eliminate AFJ.

The king then had 3 daughters who received 1 extra chest each, leaving 14 for the families. With the age order FAJ, the death of Albert's or Joseph's child would reduce the number available to

15 or 16 respectively, so we must eliminate FAJ. We are left then with AJF, which is reduced from 17 to 14 by the death of Albert's child only.

(19) **Pastry-Cutter**

The forty-five pieces into which the circle may be cut are shown below:

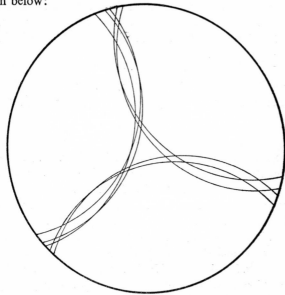

The first three cuts (or arcs) may be so arranged that each intersects the other two in two places. Moreover, every subsequent arc can intersect every arc of its own sector once, and every arc of its opposing sectors twice. Now each cut produces as many *extra* pieces as one less than the number of intersections it makes (counting its intersections with the edge of the circle itself).

We may therefore tabulate our results thus:

Cut Number	0	1	2	3	4	5	6	7
Intersections	0	2	4	6	7	9	11	12
Extra Pieces	0	1	3	5	6	8	10	11
Total Pieces	1	2	5	10	16	24	34	45

Solutions

The table could be continued indefinitely. Notice however that after every group of three successive cuts, the next cut creates only one extra piece *more* than the extra pieces of the previous cuts (instead of two extra pieces more).

(20) **Share Prices**

O.B.T.s, 9s. 4d. Geomercantiles, 6s. 8d. Addingtons, 17s. 4d.

The 'unbalanced' packet would have contained 210 shares. The final packet contained therefore $210 - 60 = 150$ (i.e. 75 O.B.T.s and 75 Addingtons).

The three equations are therefore:

$105x + 75y + 30z = 60(x + y + z) = 75(x + z) = 100$, which may be solved simultaneously to give $x = £\frac{7}{15}$, $y = £\frac{1}{3}$, $z = £\frac{13}{15}$.

(21) **Digital Wanderers**

The smallest possible amount is £235,697 14s. 8d. (each of the fathers contributing £21,427, and each of the sons 1s. 4d.). The largest possible amount is £9,856,231 7s. 4d.

To keep the total below £1m. the boys' donation must exceed 10s. Now since 11 and 240 are mutually prime, the 'pounds' must be divisible by 11; thus the 'shillings and pence' must be also. To avoid digital repetition, the boys' donation could have been only 19s. 3d., 18s. 4d., 17s. 5d., 15s. 7d., 14s. 8d., or 13s. 9d. (but in seeking the smallest quantity the first three may be rejected as merely larger digital variables of the last three). Now if the boys' donation were 15s. 7d. the 'pounds' must be made up of the digits, 2, 3, 4, 6, 8, 9; if 14s. 8d., 2, 3, 5, 6, 7, 9; if 13s. 9d., 2, 4, 5, 6, 7, 8.

In each case the total of the digits is 32, therefore, remembering the rule given in the Lead, the three digits in the odd places must (like the three digits in the even places) equal 16, or the one group must equal 5 and the other 27. Obviously, any of the three digits will add up to more than 5, so we may ignore this possibility, and concentrate on each group totalling 16. In the first group 2, 6, 8 ($= 16$) are obviously the best odd-place digits, and 3, 4, 9, the even, giving 236489. Similarly the second group gives 235697, and the third 246587. The second combination is the lowest of

Solutions

the three and, combined with the relevant 14*s*. 8*d*. gives the answer to the lowest possible figure. Similar, but reversed, reasoning produces the highest possible figure.

(22) **Calculari's Concerts**

For his last concert, Calculari played Liszt, Brahms, Mozart, and Chopin, in that order.

Since Beethoven and Mozart were never played in the same concert, one of these must always have been excluded. Consequently every concert must have included Brahms, Chopin, and Liszt, and (because of the inclusion of Brahms) Liszt must have started each concert. Then, if Beethoven were omitted, since in such cases Mozart must immediately be followed by Chopin, these two composers can fill only (a) second and third, or (b) third and fourth places respectively, and (since Brahms must fill the other place) these are the only two possible alternatives in a non-Beethoven concert. Similarly, if Mozart were omitted (Brahms consequently finishing the programme) Beethoven and Chopin can fill only (c) second and third, or (d) third and second places respectively. Only four arrangements are therefore possible, and three of these, viz. (a), (c), and (d) result in Brahms finishing the concert. These three cases must therefore have accounted for Calculari's first three concerts. (b) must have been his last concert.

(23) **A Safe Number**

Quaddle's number was 102564 which, when multiplied by its final digit (4) gives 410256, i.e. the original number with the 4 transferred to the other end.

Since, apart from 1 which is ruled out by the problem, there are only eight digits, there can be only eight such basic numbers with this peculiarity. The example suggested in the Lead may be worked out thus:

$8 \times 8 = 64$. Therefore 'h' is 4. Replace 'h' by 4, both in the multiplicand and the product, and continue: $8 \times 4 = 32$ (+ 6, carried over) = 38. Therefore 'g' is 8, and so on. Continue in this manner until the first two digits of the multiplicand read 10

85

Solutions

(because if, by a similar process 8abcd....efgh were to be divided by 8, the first two digits in the quotient must be 10).

Similar numbers may be discovered for each of the eight digits 2, 3, 4, 5, 6, 7, 8, 9 and these numbers contain 18, 28, 6, 42, 58, 22, 13, 44 digits respectively. The smallest is therefore that for 4 (only six digits).

Further such numbers may be devised by repeating any of the basic numbers so obtained any number of times. To take 4 as an example, $102564102564102564 \times 4 = 410256410256410256$.

(24)   **Court Cards**

The number of moves required for the Court Cards is 31, for a Piquet suit 255, and for a Bridge suit 8,191.

The first two results could possibly be obtained empirically, but the sheer labour of the task rules out the practicability of moving a whole Bridge suit while counting the moves. The answer may, however, be obtained quite easily if one notices that in all cases the number of moves required is $2^n - 1$, where n equals the number of cards. Thus, if we were to apply this formula to a whole stack of 52 ranked cards, we can see that it would take no less than 4,503,599,627,370,495 moves to complete the transfer, a job that would take several million years.

The method of moving an *odd* number of cards in order to achieve the minimum result is: Move the Ace *clockwise* one circle. Move the next highest exposed card to the other circle. Continue this process over and over again until stacking is completed. For an *even* number of cards the Ace must go anti-clockwise.

This problem is almost identical with the ancient *Tower of Hanoi* puzzle, but I have left it in this book since it provides an ideal substitute for Patience or Chequers if one should tire of those games.

(25)   **Long Division**

403,200 of the 3,265,920 numbers are divisible by 72.

From the rules given in the Lead it is obvious that if we can determine how many of the 3,265,920 numbers are divisible by

Solutions

both 8 and 9 (which are mutually prime) our problem will be solved.

All the 3,265,920 numbers formed by the digits 0–9 will be divisible by 9, because these ten digits total 45, and 45 is divisible by 9 (see Lead). We may therefore concentrate on 8.

There are just 88 numbers between 001 and 999 which are divisible by 8 (see Lead for the Rule of 8) and which do not repeat a digit, therefore every one of the numbers we seek must end with one of these 88 three-figure groups. If written out (016, 024, 032, 048, ... etc.) it will be seen that, of these 88, 32 contain zero and the remaining 56 do not.

Consider first the 32 three-figure groups containing zero. Each of the 32 groups may be prefixed with the remaining seven digits in any order (for zero is safely tucked away towards the end of the number) i.e. in $7 \times 6 \times 5 \times 4 \times 3 \times 2 \times 1 = 5,040$ ways. $32 \times 5,040 = 161,280$ possible numbers.

Now consider the 56 non-zero groups. Here the zero is free to wander towards the front of the number so, instead of having seven digits to choose from as the first digit in the number we have only six, since zero must not appear at the beginning. The 56 non-zero groups may therefore be prefixed in $6 \times 6 \times 5 \times 4 \times 3 \times 2 \times 1 = 4,320$ ways, giving another $56 \times 4,320 = 241,920$ possible numbers. $161,280 + 241,920 = 403,200$.

(26)   **Riddleton By-Election**

The results of the by-election were: Conservative 18,892, Liberal 10,997, Labour 9,767, Independent 5,775, Communist 825.

At the 1955 election, if we take the Conservative's absolute majority from his majority over Labour we get $4,977 - 2,335 = 2,642$ which must have been the vote received by the third candidate. The total vote at that election may be represented as: Labour $\frac{2}{5}$ + Conservative $(\frac{2}{5} + 4,977)$ + Third candidate 2,642. Therefore $4,977 + 2,642 (= 7,619)$ must have accounted for $\frac{1}{5}$ of the poll, making the number voting 38,095. Simple percentage calculations now show that in 1955 there were 50,125 on the roll, which increased to 52,864 for the by-election, of which number

Solutions

46,256 voted. At the by-election therefore 5,782 votes were needed to save a deposit. Mr. Freer got within 10 of this number, but his votes were a multiple 7. 5,775 is the only number that will satisfy this condition (giving the Communist 825). Subtracting the Independent and Communist vote from the total poll we get 39,656, to which we must add the Conservative's majority over the Liberal (7,895) together with the Conservative's majority over Labour (9,125) and divide the total by the number of candidates yet undetermined (i.e. 3) to get the Conservative vote of 18,892. Having arrived at this figure, the rest follows by simple subtraction.

(27)   **A Matter of X-ercise**

The round trip was 22 miles.

Two considerations could make possible the equation given in the Lead which, incidentally, is a perfectly legitimate assumption since Mr. Quation's eitherway walk between B and C must always occupy $2\frac{1}{2}$ hours.

Of the two possibilities, the one that springs most readily to mind is that the distance A–B = the distance C–A. This leads to a solution: A–B = 4m., B–C = 10m., C–A = 4m., Total = 18m., an answer that is quite wrong because the 10-mile road joining B and C is straight and, however straight we were to make the two 4-mile roads leading from B and C, they could never both reach A.

The other, perhaps less obvious, alternative is that the *speeds* of horse and bike are the same (viz. 12 m.p.h.) and this assumption solves the problem with A–B = 8m., B–C = 10m., C–A = 4m., Total = 22m.

Anyone who worked algebraically calling A–B a miles, C–A b miles, horse-speed x m.p.h., bike-speed y m.p.h. was open to the same pitfall when reaching the stage of saying $ay + cx = ax + cy$. This may be factorized as $a(y-x) = c(y-x)$ from which it follows that $a = c$, thus leading to the erroneous solution. It should be noticed that the equation may also be factorized as $y(a-c) = x(a-c)$ from which it follows that $y = x$.

88

(28)   **Rookery**

There are 3,432 equally short routes. Consider the diagram:

Start	a	b	c	d	e	f	g
1	1	1	1	1	1	1	1
h 1	i 2	j 3	k 4	5	6	7	8
		6	10	15	21	28	36
			20	35	56	84	120
				70	126	210	330
					252	462	792
						924	1716
							3432

Obviously there is only one direct route by which the Rook can reach any one square on the top line or in the left-hand column. Now in order to reach 'i' he can approach through either 'a' or 'h', giving two possible routes. Similarly to reach 'j' he must approach through either 'b' or 'i'. There is only one way of reaching 'b' and two of reaching 'i', so he may arrive at 'j' in a total of three ways. The number of equally short routes to any square is therefore the sum of the number of routes to the squares immediately above it and immediately to the left of it. The process of calculation for squares lying on the diagonal may, however, be shortened by noticing that the figure for a diagonal square is exactly twice that for the square lying immediately above it. It is quite an easy task to complete the square as shown.

(29)   **Pin-Pointing Sabotage**

The drawing-pin travelled exactly one mile.

If we call the diameter of the wheel *d* then, according to the

Solutions

rule give in the Lead, the length of each cycloid arch will be $4d$. Also the circumference of the wheel will be πd.

Let us call the diameter of the track D. Then the circumference of the track will be πD, and in circling the track once the wheel will make $\dfrac{\pi D}{\pi d}$ i.e. $\dfrac{D}{d}$ revolutions. Since the pin (following the path of the cycloid) will travel a distance of $4d$ for each revolution, in $\dfrac{D}{d}$ revolutions it will travel $\dfrac{D \times 4d,}{d}$ i.e. $4D$, which simply means 4 times the diameter of the track. To multiply $\tfrac{1}{4}$ mile by 4 is only half a second's work. Similarly, if the track were, say, 1 mile in diameter, the pin would travel 4 miles, and so on, irrespective of the size of the wheel. Since the two arches of the cycloid are symmetrical, the formula will always hold good provided the wheel completes an exact number of revolutions or an exact number of revolutions plus half a revolution in which latter case the pin must start at the bottom and finish at the top or vice versa.

In practice minute variations would occur on account of both the tangential offset of the wheel from the circumference of the track and the amount the wheel tilted inwards. Both these considerations (which in any case would account for a mere fraction of an inch in the whole circuit) were ruled out in the problem.

(30) **Pip Poker**

The hands were made up as follows: (a) 6, 6, 4, 2, 2; (b) 6, 6, 3, 3, 2; (c) 6, 5, 5, 2, 2; (d) 5, 5, 4, 3, 3.

The total number of pips on all cards was 80. Each child must therefore have held 20 pips.

Since there were 5 Sixes, at least one child must have had 2 of them (totalling 12 pips) and his other 3 cards must have included at least 1 Two (but could not have included a Five).

Assume the other three children each had 1 Six. Then at least one of these three must have had 2 Fives (because the first child had no Five) Now a child with a Six and 2 Fives could complete his 20 only with 2 Twos. No other child could then have had 2 Fives also (for he could complete his hand in only the same

90

Solutions

way). Therefore the last two children would have each 1 Six and 1 Five. Now one of these last must have had at least 1 Two, and could therefore make up his 20 only with a Three and a Four. The remaining Two would have to be allocated (along with a Four) to the very first child (who already has 1 Two) but this would leave the last child to take 3 Threes, and no other child had three-of-a-kind. Therefore we cannot assume that '*the other three children each had 1 Six*'.

We must assume that two children each had 2 Sixes. Similarly it may be shown that the other two children each had 2 Fives, and that the one lacking a Six must also have had 2 Threes and so on.

Of course, one may hit on the answer to such a problem by mere trial and error, but the sort of reasoning outlined above will enable you to prove that the answer given is the only possible one.

(31)   **Running to Time**

Tom ran exactly 2 miles. Trying to work out the exact size of the small square field only involves one in deep fractional waters, and is quite unnecessary. Farmer Roots's name refers not to horticultural roots, but to the mathematical variety.

One side of the small field is obviously $\sqrt{2}-1$ miles, so using the notation suggested in the Lead, M (the distance the farmer walked) is $2.\sqrt{2}-2$ miles, and the total distance run by Tom we have called D miles.

Now when Tom caught up with his father, the farmer had walked $\frac{1}{2}(D-M)$ miles *in exactly the same time* that Tom had run $\frac{1}{2}(D+M)$ miles. Similarly, for the whole distance, the farmer walked M miles while Tom ran D miles. Therefore since their relative speeds were constant $\dfrac{D}{M}=\dfrac{\frac{1}{2}(D+M),}{\frac{1}{2}(D-M)}$ i.e. $\dfrac{D}{M}=\dfrac{D+M}{D-M}$. Cross-multiplying this last equation we get $D(D-M)=M(D+M)$, or $D^2-DM=DM+M^2$, which means $D^2-2DM=M^2$. Complete the square by adding M^2 to both sides, and we get $D^2-2DM+M^2=2M^2$. Extract the square root of both sides to obtain $D-M=\sqrt{2}M$, i.e. $D=\sqrt{2}M+M$ or, in other words, $D=M(\sqrt{2}+1)$. We

91

may now resubstitute $2\sqrt{2}-2$ for M, which gives us

$$D=(2\sqrt{2}-2)\,(\sqrt{2}+1).$$

The $\sqrt{2}$ multiplies itself out leaving us simply with D=2.

(32)   **Checking Precedent**

In order to complete the transfer in the minimum number of 70 moves, the pieces must move to and fro between the palaces in the following order:

Q, K, QR, Q, KR, K, Q, K, QB, Q, K, QR, Q, K, KB, K, KR, K, QR, Q, KR, K, Q, K, QKt, Q, K, QR, Q, KR, K, Q, K, QB, Q, K, QR, Q, KR, K, Q, K, KKt, K, KR, K, Q, K, KB, K, KR, K, Q, K, QB, Q, K, QR, Q, K, KB, K, KR, K, QR, Q, KR, K, Q, K.

If one solves the problem using smaller numbers of pieces, taking care to notice sequences repeated in each case, it may be noticed that the number of moves required for N pieces (which we may call N_m moves) is equal to

$$(N-1)_m+(N-2)_m-(N-3)_m+2(N-4)_m+2.$$

(33)   **Barber's Pole**

Each fly would have travelled $26\frac{1}{4}$ inches.

If, as suggested in the Lead, we were to split the pole down the centre from x to y and roll it out flat, we should have a simple rectangle which would look like this:

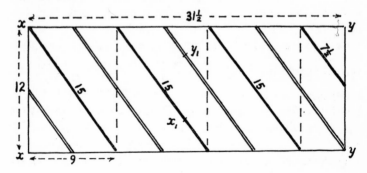

Solutions

The base of the large triangle on the left will be $31\frac{1}{2} \div 3\frac{1}{2} =$ 9 inches. Its height will be the circumference of the pole, i.e. 12 inches. It is therefore a 3 : 4 : 5 right-angled triangle, giving 15 inches for its hypotenuse. The total length of the heavy black (or gold) line is therefore $15+15+15+7\frac{1}{2}=52\frac{1}{2}$ inches. Since the silver line is of the same length, the flies will obviously be equidistant from either end when each has completed half its journey, i.e. $26\frac{1}{4}$ inches. They will then be at the points shown in the diagram as x_1 and y_1.

(34)   **Noughts and Crosses**

1,884 diagrams would be needed to represent all legitimate games.

Let us assume that 'Cross' starts the play. Then the diagram representing the final position can contain only: (A) 3 Xs and 2 Os, (B) 3 Xs and 3 Os, (C) 4 Xs and 3 Os, (D) 4 Xs and 4 Os, (E) 5 Xs and 4 Os. Any other combinations would mean that someone had missed a turn.

As an example, consider the case of 4 Xs and 4 Os, with reference to diagram (i) below:

(i)   (ii)

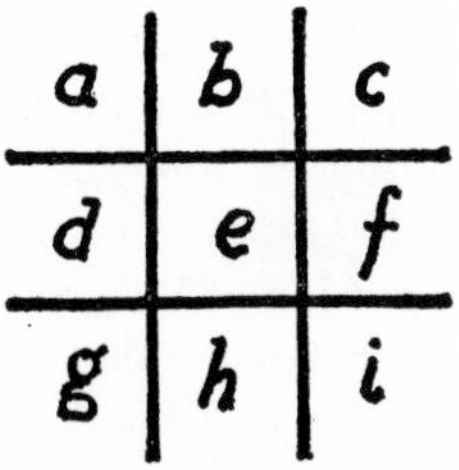

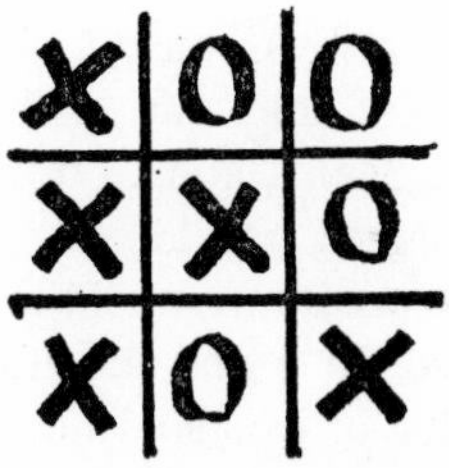

There are 6 *lateral* winning combinations for three of the Os. *abc, def, ghi, adg, beh, cfi*. In each case there are 6 squares that may be occupied by the remaining O giving $6\times6=36$ 'patterns' that may be formed by the Os. Now for each of these 36 'O patterns' there will be 3 *non-winning* combinations for X (e.g. if the Os fill places *abcd*, the four Xs can be shown in *efgh, efgi,* or *efhi* (any other X positions such as *eghi* or *fghi* would give X a win, and a pattern showing a win for both X and O must be illegiti-

93

Solutions

mate). Therefore when O wins such a game laterally, $36 \times 3 = 108$ diagrams will be needed. Similarly for the 2 *diagonal* winning combinations of O, a further 60 diagrams will be needed, giving a total of 168 diagrams for a game showing 4 Xs and 4 Os.

In a similar manner the number of legitimate combinations for each type of diagram may be obtained and summarized as (A) 120, (B) 148, (C) 444, (D) 168, (E) 62, totalling 942 diagrams for games started by 'Cross'. But there is a similar number of legitimate transpositions for games started by 'Nought', giving a grand total of 1,884.

Care must be taken in the case of 5 Xs and 4 Os, otherwise instances such as that illustrated in diagram (ii) above may be wrongly excluded on the grounds that 'Cross' has already won, say, vertically before claiming his diagonal win. However 'Cross' could win such a game quite legitimately if the top left-hand X were the last symbol inserted. In such a case he would win simultaneously on two lines, and such a diagram must be considered as representing a possible legitimate win.

(35)   **Multiple Motors**

The Grimsby Grouse, Oxbridge, Angerley, Nomad, and Engout Seven, were sold during the morning. The Straitley, Cheetah, Daleman Manx, and Cottonsley, during the afternoon. The Ensign remained unsold.

Since the cars were sold in the proportion of 1 : 2, the morning accounted for $\frac{1}{3}$ and the afternoon for $\frac{2}{3}$ of the day's sales. The total value of cars sold must therefore be divisible by 3. Now it will make the task of eliminating the unsold car much simpler if we remember that, in order for a number to be divisible by 3, the sum of its digits must be divisible by 3. The grand total for all cars is £2,791, the sum of whose digits is 19. Of the ten prices, only one (£124) has a digital sum (in this case 7) which, when subtracted from 19 leaves a number divisible by 3 (viz. 12). This then is the sum which must be excluded from the day's sales. Subtracting this sum from the total we get £2,667, one-third of which is £889 (the morning's sales) and two-thirds of which is

£1,778 (the afternoon's sales). Obviously the £860 Straitley cannot be included in the morning total, and must be subtracted from the afternoon's £1,778, leaving £918 which must include at least one of the £425 cars. Similar reasoning will enable one to assign each of the cars to either the morning or afternoon sales.

(36)   **Circle of Fate**

Algebar was the very man to whom the king had given the gold cross and, needless to say, the Princess Problema wore it ever after as a memento of the happy day.

If you happened to follow the suggestion given in the lead, you should have finished up with a table something like this in which the number of men in a circle is given in bold figures, and the position in which a man must stand in order to be the last remaining in a straightforward count (of 'Three') is given below.

3	**4**	**5**	**6**	**7**	**8**	**9**	**10**	**11**	**12**	**13**	**14**	**15**	**16**	**17**
2	1	4	1	4	7	1	4	7	10	13	2	5	8	11

Notice that the bottom row is obtained by adding 3 to each previous figure (and deducting the number standing above it if that number happens to be smaller than the result). Now it follows from the story that, had there been n men left when Problema reversed the direction of counting, Algebar must have been in position $n-2$ calculated from the place at which the anti-clockwise count commenced. We must therefore find a place in the above table where the figure in the top line and the figure in the bottom differ by 2. This condition is satisfied by the 6th pair from the right ($12 - 10 = 2$), and this means that Algebar must have been the 6th man to be threatened by dismissal during the first clockwise count, and this 6th man would (in a circle of 17) have been the man with the cross.

No other position can possibly meet the requirements of the problem unless we assume that the number of men had been reduced by the clockwise count to 2, and this is ruled out by the words 'there were still quite a number of men left'.

Solutions

A Piece of Cake

The diagram shows how the cake may be divided into nine pieces which may be fitted together with no great difficulty to form five small, square cakes each having a side of $1/\sqrt{5}$ that of the original cake. That the resultant squares are, indeed, the correct dimensions may be proved by calculating the dimensions of the right-angled triangles as marked.

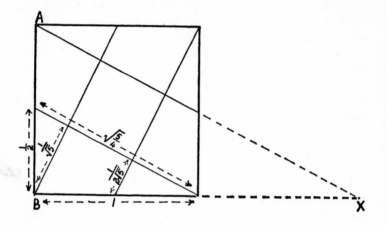

The divisions are made by joining each corner of the cake to the middle point of one of the opposite sides in cyclic order.

How to approach such a problem? An inspired guess may yield an answer, but some readers may be interested to know the line of argument I followed in order to reach this solution.

If we are to establish a quantity like $1/\sqrt{5}$ it will obviously be to our advantage if we can first establish the much simpler quantity $\sqrt{5}$. This may be done quite simply by extending the base line to double its original length, so that AB=1, and BX=2. AX is then $\sqrt{1^2+2^2}=\sqrt{5}$. Now $1/\sqrt{5}$ is one-fifth of $\sqrt{5}$. In order to get the side of our small square we must therefore divide the line AX into five equal parts, a procedure which produces the dissection shown in the diagram.

Solutions

Extensive Reasoning

The club should have paid exactly £20, for it may be shown that the area of the shaded crescent in the original diagram is exactly the same as the area of the rectangle formed (as suggested in the Lead) by joining A to C, and E to G.

The total area of the figure bounded by the points AEFGC is equal to the area of the semicircle EFG plus the rectangle AEGC. Again, the total area is also equal to the semicircle ABC plus the crescent AFCB. But the area of the semicircle EFG equals the area of the semicircle ABC, therefore the area of the crescent must be equal to the area of the rectangle, which is 110 yards × 22 yards=2,420 square yards or half an acre. At £40 per acre this would then cost £20.

Doubtless, however, the club secretary's son reasoned, with less mathematical elegance, but just as validly, thus: The effect of the change was merely to pick up the semicircle ABC and carry it out to EFG, sandwiching in the rectangle to fill up the space. All that has therefore been added to the area of the field is the area represented by the rectangle.

(39)   **Gifts of the Magi**

Gaspar was carrying the Frankincense, Melchior the Myrrh, and Balthazar the Gold. The three men spoken to were all lying servants.

A table such as that suggested in the Lead would look something like this:

	1	2	3	4	5	6
GASPAR	G	G	M	M	F	F
MELCHIOR	M	F	G	F	G	M
BALTHAZAR	F	M	F	G	M	G

Consider the distribution suggested in the first column. In this case Balthazar's statement that he has no Gold is evidence of his truthfulness. Then, because the truthful Balthazar vouches for Melchior, Melchior must himself be truthful. But Melchior has claimed to be the carrier of the Frankincense—an impossible claim for a truthful man carrying the Myrrh. Therefore the first column cannot represent the true state of affairs.

Similarly, columns 2, 3, 4, and 5 may be disposed of, leaving column 6 as the true one. In this case Balthazar, and therefore Melchior too are liars, and we cannot believe Melchior's statement to the effect that Gaspar had denied having the Gold. In other words Gaspar *had* claimed to have the gold. Gaspar was therefore also a liar for he was carrying the Frankincense.

(40)   **Crossnumber**

^{A}6	^{B}7	^{C}2	^{D}2	^{E}2	^{F}8	^{G}2
^{H}2	6	^{J}3	1	9	5	5
^{J}5	8	1	^{K}6	8	5	^{L}9
^{M}7	5	8	3	6	^{N}9	8
7	^{O}1	9	^{P}9	5	6	^{Q}7
1	^{R}9	0	1	^{S}1	0	9
^{T}1	6	0	2	1	^{U}4	9

Since N dn=N ac^2, and the initial digit is common, N ac= 95/6/7/8/9, but L dn is even ∴ N ac=96/8, but if the former then U ac would be 6? making L dn three-figured. ∴ N ac=98, and N dn=9604 making L dn 88 or 98. The last digit of K ac being 8 or 9, its cube root (O ac) must be 12 or 19. If the former, then K ac is 1728 making K dn 1???? (which, multiplied by 5 would make I ac only four-figured). ∴ O ac=19, making K ac 6859, I ac 3???0/5, and U ac 49 (also F dn=855, viz. $7^3 + 8^3$, these being the only two consecutive digits the sum of whose cubes exceeds 100 and ends in 5). O dn must then be 147 or 196, making R ac 40??04 or 90??09, making Q dn ?99 or ?49.

Solutions

Now P ac=I $dn \times 2$ or 3. If the former, then P ac= ??68, making the digital sum of Q dn 26 or 21 (impossible since G dn= ?0 or ?5). ∴ P ac=I $dn \times 3$, making P ac 9?67, making K dn 6?90/1 (its last digit cannot be more than 1 for then the second last digit of I ac would be more than 5). But if K dn is 6?90, R ac being palindromic, S dn would be 0? (impossible). ∴ K dn=6?91, making G dn 25 and Q dn 799, making R ac 901109, and O dn 19? (i.e. 196). The second digit of I dn cannot be more than 2, ∴ J ac= ??0/1/2, but (being a factor of the odd K dn) J ac must itself be odd, i.e. ??1, S dn is 11, and J ac is 581.

Now T ac is of the form ?6??1, but cannot be 26??1 for B dn and M dn each have only four digits, and A dn only three). It is therefore 16??1. Again A dn has been established as ??5, it can be only 125 (5³), 225 (15²), or 625 (25² or 5⁴) and is therefore of the form ?25. Then B dn is ??85 (for T ac ends in 1 as does M dn). Then H ac must be either 24 or 26. If 24, then B dn would be ?485, and M dn ?461 and, since their difference would be merely 24, they would both begin with the same digit. If that digit were 7 or less, T ac could not exceed 15???. If that digit were 8 or more, T ac would be at least 17???? (for the lowest possible quantity of A dn is 125). But T ac is 16??1 ∴ H ac cannot be 24. It must be 26, making B dn ?685, and M dn ?711. The common digit of B dn and M dn must then be 7. Therefore A dn must be 625 for neither 125 nor 225 would bring the total of T ac up to 16??1.

The only true factor of U ac is 7, therefore this is also the true factor of D dn which must be ?1 (for I ac can now be fully established). D dn is then either 81 or 21, but (now that we have established the first digit of M ac) it must be 21. The remainder of the problem can now be solved by simple addition and subtraction.

(41)   **Pledge's Letter**

Mr. Pledge (his real name, incidentally, was Mr. Pawn) rightly interpreted the postscript as meaning that the sixty-four words of the message were to be written in the form of a square and, to an enthusiastic member of the Mudmarsh Chess Club, this 8×8 square immediately suggested a chessboard. Moreover the words 'check whenever need arises' seemed to imply some form of chess move, and Mr. Pledge noticed that the word 'need' occurs twice in the message. The obvious square to be checked is the one containing the word 'Rex' (which stands for 'king'), and the only piece that could check this square from both the 'need' squares is the knight, represented (so Mr. Pledge reasoned) by the word 'Sir' in the top left-hand corner.

The knight from this square must therefore 'get a move on' to visit every square, finishing up on the word 'plan' (the only remaining square from which he can 'check again at the end too'). There are several ways in which this can be done, but only one that makes sense, viz.:

(Sir) AN ATTEMPT TO LAND AT PORTLAND BILL ONE MORNING DURING MAY IS NOW ALL BUT CERTAIN. THEIR HIGH COMMAND REGARDS IT AS POSSIBLE BASE. AS FOR CRAFT THEY HAVE ALL THEY NEED, AND AWAIT ONLY A DARK NIGHT WITH WEATHER CONDITIONS OF THE RIGHT KIND. YOU WILL NEED TO KEEP A CLOSE WATCH ON DEAL TOO WHICH ALSO FIGURES IN THEIR PLAN. (Rex).

The references in the postscript to 'stopping' refer to punctuation.

(42) **Crow-Flight**

From the petrol station to Mainstead is a distance of 25 miles.

$$XO = \frac{a+11}{2} \text{ and } OP = \frac{a-11}{2}^*$$. And since MP=a, by Pythagoras

we have $c^2 = a^2 - \frac{(a-11)^2}{2}.$

Then $b^2 = \frac{4a^2 + 44a}{4},$ i.e. $b^2 = a^2 + 11a.$

Now the problem implies that both a and b must be integers. Then, since 11 is prime, and its parts are 5+6, a must be equal to 5^2, from which it follows that $b=30$.

(43)   **Betting to Win**

Harbockle placed his bets as follows: KNOW HOW £216, ACROSTIC £288, MY ZERO £384, EQUATION £432, ADVANTAGE £864, CALCULATION £1,152.

An examination of any list of odds will show that *If the sum of the reciprocals of one more than each of the odds is less than 1, it is possible so to place bets that one is absolutely sure of winning.*

Thus, adding 1 to each of the odds given, we get 16, 12, 9, 8, 4, 3. Adding the reciprocals (i.e. the corresponding fractions) we get $\frac{1}{16}+\frac{1}{12}+\frac{1}{9}+\frac{1}{8}+\frac{1}{4}+\frac{1}{3}=\frac{139}{144}$ which is less than 1. We can therefore so place bets to be sure of winning $1-\frac{139}{144}=\frac{5}{144}$ of the total moneys to be received (or $\frac{5}{139}$ of the moneys staked).

Now Harbockle wished to win £120, i.e. 24 times 5. He therefore had to receive from the bookmaker 24 times 144=£3,456. In order to receive this in the event of the first horse winning he would obviously have to lay $\frac{1}{16}$ of this amount, i.e. £216; getting from the bookmaker £216×15 plus his original stake of £216 =£3,456. Similarly for the second horse he must place $\frac{1}{12}$ of £3,456, i.e. £288, and so on. The total of all such stakes will be £3,336 which is £120 less than the amount he *must* receive from the bookmaker irrespective of which horse wins.

(Note that a price like 5 to 2 is really $2\frac{1}{2}$ to 1, and 1 more than this is $3\frac{1}{2}$ to 1, or 7 to 2, the reciprocal of which is $\frac{2}{7}$.)

---

* Notice that OP could also equal $\frac{11-a}{2}$ (should P lie west of O) but since $(11-a)^2 = (a-11)^2$ this cannot affect the resulting equations.

Solutions

Unfortunately bookmakers (though they may not actually calculate in this way) usually so choose their odds that the adjusted reciprocals add up to more than 1. Only once have I seen a list of odds in which this was not so and, at the time, I had only about 15s. in my pocket, for which outlay I could have won something less than a farthing.

(44)   **Divide and Conquer**

Puzzooloo could have achieved his object only by allocating the provinces in the following manner:

To the Blackers, 1, 6, 8, 10, 14. To the Stipplers, 2, 11, 13, 17, 18. To the Hachures, 3, 5, 12, 16, 19. To the Chequers, 4, 7, 9, 15, 20.

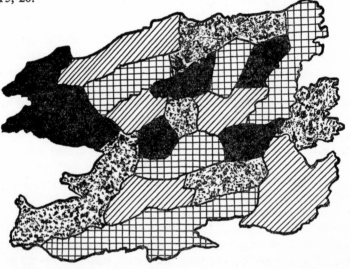

Without the restriction on the allocation of the area numbered 16, there would be 119 solutions to the problem. When this problem first appeared, the considerable task of calculating by hand the whole of the 119 solutions was undertaken by Mr. John Wilmers of Oxford. His solutions tallied exactly with the 119 produced by EDSAC II, the Cambridge University automatic computer which had been programmed for the task by Mr. John H.

Solutions

Matthewman of Cambridge. It was the computer sheet of EDSAC II which revealed the unique determination properties of area No. 16.

(45)   **Crown and Anchor**

In Crown and Anchor, the bank may expect to win $\frac{17}{216}$ of all moneys staked (roughly 1*s*. out of every 13*s*.).

Assuming that there is 1*s*. on each of the six squares each throw, the banker will then pay out 3*s*. each time. However in the case of Singletons (all three dice different) he will collect 3*s*. off losing squares, in the case of Doubletons (a pair plus one odd die) 4*s*. off losing squares, and in the case of Trebletons (three dice of a kind) 5*s*. off losing squares.

Now, whatever way the first die may fall, the remaining two can fall in 36 different ways. For instance, should the first die fall Spades, the various possible combinations could be tabulated thus.

SSS	SHS	SDS	SCS	SCS	SAS
SSH	SHH	SDH	SCH	SCH	SAH
SSD	SHD	SDD	SCD	SCD	SAD
SSC	SHC	SDC	SCC	SCC	SAC
SSC	SHC	SDC	SCC	SCC	SAC
SSA	SHA	SDA	SCA	SCA	SAA

From such a table it will be seen that, out of every 36 throws, the chances are that 1 will be a Trebleton (the very first entry in the table) 15 will be Doubletons (they have been underlined in the table) and the remaining 20 will be Singletons. On the Trebleton, the bank will pay out 3*s*. and collect 5*s*.; on the 15 Doubletons, it will pay out 45*s*. and collect 60*s*. On the 20 Singletons, it will pay out 60*s*. and collect 60*s*.

Over a typical run of 36 throws, the bank will therefore pay out a total of 108*s*. and collect a total of 125*s*., a profit of 17*s*., during a period when punters will have laid on the cloth a total of $36 \times 6s. = 216s.$

Solutions

46

Casting Up

Thirty-seven applicants were turned down by letter.

The problem could, of course, be worked arithmetically but this is a good example of the sort of problem that lends itself to a graphical approach.

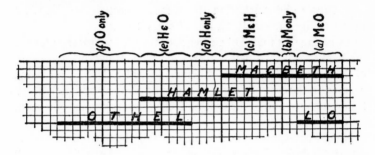

Make c (actors who have played both M and H) 1 unit in length. Then M's line will be 2 units. O's line will total 3 units, and a quarter of its total length (i.e. $\frac{3}{4}$ unit) will fill up a leaving $\frac{1}{4}$ unit for b. d will then be $\frac{1}{2}$ unit and, from d we may draw the remaining $2\frac{1}{4}$ units of O's line. This gives an overall length of $4\frac{3}{4}$ units, representing the total number interviewed. H's line must therefore be extended to total a half of this, i.e. $2\frac{3}{8}$ units, leaving $1\frac{3}{8}$ units for f (those who have played only O).

Now $1\frac{3}{8}$ is $\frac{11}{38}$ of $4\frac{3}{4}$. Therefore, in order to avoid slicing men into pieces (for, as was pointed out in the Lead, the producer had no ambition to play Shylock) the whole group must comprise 38 men (it could not be a multiple of 38, for then the interviewed group would exceed the total number of applicants). With 38 interviewed, $75 - 38 = 37$ must have been the number turned down by letter.

47

Cannon Balls

1,254 balls could have been fitted into the box.

Since the area of the box (in square feet) equals the volume of the box (in cubic feet) we get, from the formulae suggested in the

Solutions

Lead: $5s^2=s^3$. Divide both sides by s^2 and get $5=s$. Therefore the box is 5 feet square. Similarly for the cannon ball, we can divide both sides of the equation $\dfrac{d^3\pi}{6}=d^2\pi$ by $d^2\pi$ to get $\dfrac{d}{6}=1$, i.e. $d=6$ meaning that the diameter of each ball is 6 inches.

Obviously, then the box could contain $10\times10\times10=1,000$ balls stacked squarely in 10 layers of 100 balls each, but this will leave a great deal of waste space represented by the interstices between the balls. A better result can be obtained by placing 100 balls on the bottom layer and each successive alternate layer with layers of 81 balls each (9×9) sandwiched in between. This permits 13 layers in all (7 of 100 each, and 6 of 81 each) giving 1,186 in all, but leaving a gap of just over 3 inches at the top, the vertical interval between the axes of successive layers being $\sqrt{2}r$.

If, however, the balls in the bottom layer are stacked triangularly (as shown in the diagram) we can fit in 6 rows of 10 each alternating with 5 rows of 9 each, making 105 for that layer. Now

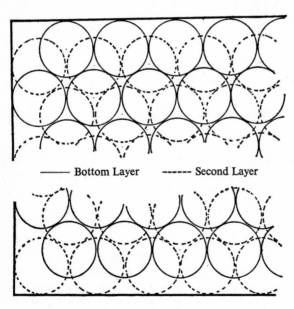

——— Bottom Layer   ------ Second Layer

Solutions

if all these rows are pushed up together towards one end of the box, the *lateral* interval between the axes of successive rows will be $\sqrt{3}r$, where r is the radius of the balls. The gap at the end of the box will then be $s—r\{2+\sqrt{3}(n—1)\}$ where n is the number of rows in the layer, viz. 11. This gap, then, will be approximately 2.04 inches, sufficient to enable us to superimpose the second layer as a 'gap to ball' reflection on the first, giving, as shown in the diagram, 6 rows of 9 balls each, and 5 rows of 10 each (104 in all for the second layer).

Ignoring the very small lateral play (only a few thousandths of an inch) still left between balls in successive layers, the *vertical* interval between the axes of successive layers will then be $\sqrt{\dfrac{8r^2}{3}}=\sqrt{24}$ inches$=4.8989$ inches. 12 layers will then reach to a height of $11 \times 4.8989+6$ inches, leaving a gap of only a little over $\frac{1}{10}$ inch at the top of the box.

We can therefore accommodate 6 layers of 105 balls each plus 6 layers of 104 balls each, totalling 1,254.

(48)   **Grave Difficulties**

Roger Galaday St. Semplice, born 1377 (MCCCLXXVII), died 1428 (MCDXXVIII). His wife, Alice, born 1393 (MCCCXCIII), died 1429 (MCDXXIX).

Obviously 1 must be added to the year of Roger's death to obtain the year of Alice's, and the result of this addition is to reduce the length of the figure by two numerals. In Roman notation, the addition of 1 reduces the number of numerals by two only in the case of VIII+1=IX. VIII and IX are therefore the last numeral groups in the death dates irrespective of what precedes them. By taking 1 from the first, and 6 from the second of these numeral groups (for Roger was 5**1**, and Mary 3**6**) we get Roger's birth-date as ???????VII, and Alice's as ??????III.

Now Roger was 16 years older than Alice (at the time of his death), therefore we must add 16 to Roger's birth-date to get Alice's. The 'tens' in her birth-date is therefore twenty more than the 'tens' in Roger's, since 7 (the last figure in her birth-date)+16

Solutions

=23, but this addition of twenty reduces the number of undefined numerals by one. This can happen only in the case of LXX+20 =XC. We now have: Roger born ????LXXVII and (by addition) died ???XXVIII. The latter must belong to the century following the former. The only possible centuries of birth are DCCC, MCCC, MDCC, and of these only MCCC shortens from ???? to ??? when increased by 100—it becomes MCD. The remaining calculations are quite straightforward.

(49)   **Close Fit**

E, H, J, K will always be surrounded by other pieces. Indeed there is only one basic way in which the pieces can be fitted together, and this way is shown in the diagram. All other arrangements will be merely rotations or reflections of this figure.

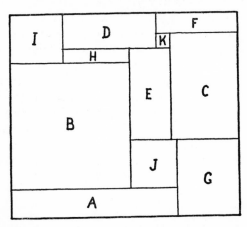

The total area of the eleven pieces is 986 square units. The only possible rectangular dimensions are therefore 2 × 493, 58 × 17, or 34 × 29. Obviously, only the last of these would accommodate the 18 × 18 square B. Mark out a 34 × 29 rectangle.

Now if A were to lie vertically, a total area of 4 × 4 units would remain at its end (or ends). H and K (the only other pieces whose widths total 4 units) cannot fill the gap (or gaps) for K is too short. Therefore A cannot lie vertically. Place B (with the horizontal A) anywhere on the area and consider C. C cannot lie horizontally for it would then leave a gap of 1 unit between itself and B (and no piece of 1 unit width exists). Therefore C lies vertically.

With A, B, and C thus roughly placed, E must lie *between* B and C, and C must be at least two units higher or lower than B. G must occupy a corner position at the end of A (but not touching B).

The fitting of the remaining pieces becomes progressively easier if the sequence suggested in the Lead is followed.

(50)   **An 'Insoluble' Problem**

In the regiment were 7 officers (excluding the Colonel) and 49 sergeants. The maximum number of privates permitted to be under the command of a sergeant was 6.

A clue to the method of solution is given in the colonel's name. Since the number of privates must be a (number of officers) $\times$ b (number of sergeants under each officer) $\times$ c (number of privates under each sergeant) a, b, and c must be combinations of the prime factors of 294. These are $1\times2\times3\times7\times7$, but 1 may be ignored since it is clear from the story that each officer had more than one sergeant under his command and each sergeant more than one private. Now the remaining four factors can be divided into three groups (representing a, b, and c) in four ways, viz. 2, 3, 49; 2, 7, 21; 3, 7, 14; 6, 7, 7. In all therefore we have 21 different combinations of the factors:

	A	B	C	D	E	F	G	H	I	J	K	L	M	N	O	P	Q	R	S	T	U
a	2	2	3	3	49	49	2	2	7	7	21	21	3	3	7	7	14	14	6	7	7
b	3	49	2	49	2	3	7	21	2	21	2	7	7	14	3	14	3	7	7	6	7
c	49	3	49	2	3	2	21	7	21	2	7	2	14	7	14	3	7	3	7	7	6

Now nineteen of these combinations give different answers to the question, 'How many persons are in the regiment?' If therefore I had told you how many persons were in the regiment you would have been able to tell immediately from the above table which was the true combination—unless the number I had given was 350 because then two combinations, viz. Q and U, both produce this number. One of these two must then be the true combination.

Now had the maximum number of privates under a sergeant's command been 7 or more, this additional piece of information would still have left you unable to choose between Q and U, yet you were told that this information would have made the problem soluble. The number must therefore have been less than 7. We must therefore eliminate combination Q, leaving U as the true combination. The maximum number of privates under a sergeant's command must then be 6 in order to validate combination U.